To Mother,

With love from

Claudette

Flapdoodle,
Trust & Obey

These are going to be my 10

To the Bride

1. Flatter him.
2. Feed him.
3. Keep the house in order.
4. Make him think what you want is his idea.
5. Treat his mother as you want yours treated.

To the Groom

1. Tell her she is beautiful. Time will make you a good liar.
2. Tell her you love her. She will always doubt it.
3. Don't start an argument. You can't win it.
4. Don't tell her that her relatives are horrible. She knows it.
5. When all bills are paid divide with her what is left, that she may have the atrocities for which she longs.

Mama's thoughts couched themselves in her typical firm hand—as in these "10 Commandments for a Happy Marriage" and in her other letters in this small book.

Flapdoodle, Trust & Obey

Virginia Cary Hudson

EDITED BY CHARLES L. WALLIS

Illustrated by Richard Rosenblum

HARPER & ROW
Publishers
NEW YORK

TO MOTHER

Quam dilecta!

O Lord God of hosts, blessed is the
man that putteth his trust in thee.

—THE BOOK OF COMMON PRAYER

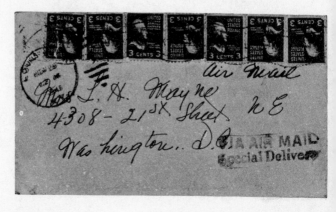

Mama seldom waited for regular mail to convey her messages. Her
flowing script, like her voluble talk, came Special Delivery to me
more often than not.—*Her Daughter Virginia.*

Contents

Preface

The ten-year-old pixie who wrote the engaging essays found in *O Ye Jigs & Juleps!* always made words and sentences dance upon a page and delighted in the magic of syntactical manipulation.

Mama combined a grace in written expression with a living grace in which her great heart embraced the hopes and anxieties, the appreciations and perplexities, and the joys and heartaches of our common humanity.

Mama often spoke of her wish to write books. Through the years she developed a contagiously blithesome and winsome manner of expression. She felt that she had something important to write for anyone who would bend an ear, and she enjoyed the prospect of transcribing her ideas wittily and cheerfully. But, alas, the exigencies of daily living, the responsibilities of maintaining a rooming house in her beloved Louisville, the various church and community tasks she readily undertook whenever called upon, and of course the labors and love of raising a family left little time for authorship.

She channeled her literary talents into the letters she wrote. In this book I have brought together several of those letters she addressed to me which best seem to mirror her enthusiasms, her philosophical and religious thinking, and her congenitally debonair spirit.

My mother's affection for people—everyone she met and knew, including those closest to her, as well as casual acquaintances or strangers—would not permit her to say or do anything which might annoy or embarrass anyone. These letters have been adapted so as to disguise individual identities and specific situations, and all names, except those of myself, my husband, and my daughter, are fictitious. Yet my mother's heart, mind, personality, and words have been preserved so that she may be as real and genuine an individual to the reader as she is to me.

Her Daughter Virginia

Mama Meets an Old Beau and Moralizes on Country Living

MY LITTLE DOVE:

The roomers have the nicest paper and the most divine pens.

I suppose you are flying about on the wings of the morning and only half doing your homey chores.

I've been dusting now for four days. I have two methods. When I feel dull, I use the feather duster. Turkeys are so unimaginative. But when I am gay, I tack my beautiful bull's tail—the one I brought back from Mexico City—to a stick.

Ah, dusting with a bull's tail! I just love that! Reminds me of luscious senoritas and my mind pictures lace mantillas draped over high combs and of sleek-haired, straight-bodied matadors in silken breeches. Swords swish and crowds cheer.

Why did the stupid bull become enraged and snort and paw away his life? If only he had just sat down, smiled, and taken it easy, everything would have been so different, and his tail wouldn't be tacked to my stick.

Sometimes, my Little Apple, all of us find ourselves in

9

the ring with the matador. Sometime soon, sometime late, but always sometimes. And the outcome depends entirely on our own conduct. If we behave as all bulls should, we would just sit down, take it easy, and wait through the dusk and even the blackest night for the dawn of another day. Then, my Little Chickadee, all of the world's matadors would be waiting in line at the unemployment office.

Do you remember my talking about Charley Jones from St. Louis? He's the one who was reported shot down and missing in the first war. Well, he called Friday, and I went downtown to have lunch with him.

He is the picture of affluence. Diamond stickpin, gray flannels, fedora, etc., etc. Has offices in Detroit, Buffalo, Chicago, New York, and Baltimore. Keeps a two-hundred-a-month apartment in Washington. Lives in Philadelphia and very much in love with his wife.

Good old fun-loving Charley! Long, long ago my mother slapped my wrists and said I was behaving as no Episcopalian child should when Charley and I won a dip-waltz contest on a public dance floor. And, heaven forbid, showing my legs! I can still hear the mellow strains of "Blue Danube" and Charley's hilarious whisperings about how ridiculous the other contesting couples were.

I waited for Charley at the Johnson elevator door. Soon a fat little old man emerged. It was Charley. He stretched out his arms and yelled so loudly everyone in the lobby could hear: "Sugar Baby, you look like the dickens! Still the most beautiful skin in the world! After thirty-five years, kiss me, Sugar Baby, kiss me."

After a resounding kiss, I looked to the side and there was the Right Reverend staring at me! I think next Sunday I'll contemplate the God-in-nature so many people talk about.

School's almost here, and the two high school teachers, Edith and Dolly, have come back to their rooms. Ah, school! and the return of books and boy friends.

My sympathies are always with the men. They see some flighty thing, and what happens? Before they know it, they are declaring their love and promising the moon. Off to the church they go where they hold hands and say sweet things.

Scarcely does the star dust settle before she wants a house and furniture and clothes and a permanent and a trip. Every day something new. He wonders how he ever got himself into such a fix.

My advice to you, Sweetie, is to sell your house and buy a strongly built and cheerful little place and let the alchemy of love transform it into a home. But don't build your nest away out in the bushes where a milkman will need a road map to find you and from where you'll have to wade in mud to get a bus. If you love the woods and must hear the birdies sing, plant yourself a tree and buy a bird in a cage.

I've been thinking of Beulah, your cousin ten times removed, who used to live across the way and always washed the kiddies' diapers to the rhythmic thud of "The Campbells Are Coming." She and her watery-eyed husband moved to the country to farm on shares. Her boy, playing in the underbrush, was mistaken for a rabbit and had an ear lopped off. Her daughter developed T.B. Her husband's back collapsed from lifting wood. The creek rose and the chickens were drowned. The pigs floated off. The cow had a calf and died. Then the calf froze to death. When what remained of the crop was divided, they owed the landlord eight dollars. Moral: never move to the country.

It is seldom that one hears as vivid and true description of oneself as the one I heard this morning. I had lain down for a few moments on the sofa in the sunroom off the kitchen. Rebekah had been stirring and humming

at the stove for some time. Then I heard her step, ever so softly, to the door and muse, "Pretty's sleeping all right." She has always called me "Pretty" for no reason at all.

In a moment she was talking on the telephone. "Hello, Margie, is that you? . . . You sound more chirper today . . . Oh, we are still cleaning. Pretty's been on her high-tail horse all day. She's had us busting wide apart when we were trying to eat. You know where Pretty should have belonged all these years? In a Dixie Show! . . . Don't know what a Dixie Show is? . . .

"Well, Pretty hasn't always been as hefty as now. Nothing really wrong now, but that tummy of hers been baby-stretched till it can't fly back . . . Oh, yes, I've known these folks all my days. When the Lord made some folks, He drained out their blood and pumped in half vinegar and half green puhsimmons juice, but not Pretty. She's not ever going to be soured down and shriveled up. She's got milk and honey in her veins . . . But Pretty is going to do the rest of her growing up in another world. Sure not in this one . . .

"Well, I've got to wash my cabbage pot and cornpone skillet. No bashful munchers in this house . . .

"Now, good-by."

The afternoon is almost gone, and I must water the soup.

Say your prayers.

Love,
Little Mama

P.S. I definitely do not like roomers' ink.

Mama Speaks at an Auxiliary Dinner and Explains White Elephants

MY LITTLE BUTTERFLY:

I'm so glad you answer the letters I never write.

A strange young man, one Bob Robertson, who needs a haircut and looks as if he has emerged from the wilderness where he ate locusts and wild honey, comes calling on my schoolmarm roomer Edith every night.

He says he wants to be a preacher, but as long as he insists on being a Baptist I am giving him no encouragement. I tell him there are too many Baptists already, and what with all the Baptists' cars crowding the roads on Sundays, the poor old Episcopalians take their lives in their hands when they cross the street to get to their own services.

Poor old Oliver has gone to heaven to live with God. No more rent, no more groceries, no more taxes, and no more gasoline. When I put on my golden slippers and knock on the Pearly Gates, good old Saint Peter will say to me: "You finally made it. Good for you!" And Michael will give me a harp and a crown with one or two stars on it—small stars maybe. I know what I am going to play on my harp, if I get one. I am going to play one tune from morning to night—"Dixie"!

The next pleasant thought is that I capitulated in a moment of weakness and promised that I would speak at the Auxiliary dinner which was held last night.

I told them that whenever I tried to speak, I stammered and usually collapsed. If I spoke, I said, I would have to write it out and read it. They said okeh and that anyway they only wanted something entertaining. I allowed that I trusted the women would not be put to sleep, but that most likely I would have something to say on my favorite theme, to wit, that the world is full of people who aren't doing one thing for anybody.

I took along as my guest an Indian woman whom I found, wrapped in a sari, in my backyard last week. She had been sent over by Mrs. James, and when I found her she was in my pink rocking chair and waiting, she explained, until I might happen to come out. She is Mrs. Valdés of Ceylon. She's been in the States only a month. Her husband is lecturing at the University.

I could think of nothing more appropriate than to take a Moslem to a Christian feast.

The Auxiliary president made an announcement before dinner to the effect that everyone was to bring a white elephant to the next meeting. Mrs. Valdés was noticeably troubled. She clutched my arm and said that white elephants are sacred in India, and what did the president mean?

The Right Reverend, who sat across the table at dinner, was entranced with Mrs. Valdés. She had, she said, attended a mission school as a child. What did she think of Christian missions? To which she was polite and reserved.

I ventured to suggest that we had so much lust and filth and misery to clean up in our cities that a visitor might wonder why we do not abide by Jesus' teachings. I

15

offered a qualified judgment that it would do us good if someone came from abroad to enlighten and awaken American Christians.

The Right Reverend seemed visibly disturbed by my brashness. Then he placidly contemplated just what Thomas Jefferson would do in a similar circumstance. Finally, he changed the topic and said he had always thought of Valdés as a Spanish rather than an Indian name. She said her grandfather had been a seafaring man.

Much of the table talk was so banal as to have surely seemed insipid to a cultured and educated woman from Ceylon. After one woman, a cultist whose name I didn't get, chatted for at least ten minutes on her recent world tour during which her friends had found some bearded spook whom they knew to be Jesus returned, I remembered that the old Cary prayer book, dated 1771, contained "a prayer for fools and madmen." I wondered why old James had been persuaded to have it omitted. Maybe now it should be reinstated, for it is badly needed.

After the program the president told me I had been "charming." Imagine that! And about one who does no more than to boil down dressed-up ecclesiastical double-talk so the fat can be removed.

By the way, my Little Chickadee, I am writing a story of the Bible for children. It will take a year to finish and will be different from all the others. But I've got my problems, what with Eve who had no mother to warn her and the devil whispering in her ear, and David who murdered a man so he could get a wife, and that woman-crazy Solomon, and that winebibbing Herod who had a grizzly beard and wore jeweled sandals. Glory be! We're told to "search the Scriptures," but I am sure the Lord expects us to use our imaginations and read between the lines.

During the business session following dinner, they eased up on me to be chairman of the Social Relations Committee. Partly because I felt like a contented cow following dinner and partly because I had my mind on my upcoming speech, the president put my name to a vote before I actually realized what was going on.

In Kentucky the Auxiliary contains the bosses and the Guild contains the workers in the churches. The Auxiliary members are the blabbers and popper-offers. The Guild attends the altar, looks after the church supplies, and sews for the hospital, orphanage, and home for unmarried mothers. The Auxiliary uses your brains, and the Guild uses your hands.

Ask your minister how his church women are organized, and then get into the group that most appeals to you.

Say your prayers.

Love,
Little Mama

Mama Contemplates the Vagaries of Mortal Life and the Felicities of Heaven

My Little Hummingbird:

A week ago I took poor, pitiful, bedridden Mrs. Amesbury back to the asylum for the second time.

On the way home I went to the cathedral and lighted a candle for her and begged the dear Lord to call her home. "Come down, Lord," I said, "and get poor old Mrs. Amesbury. She is old and withered and her wits have fled from her. Send old Gabriel after her, but if he is too busy, send someone younger. Send my own child, Lord. You came and took him from me. Tell him his mother asks him to take poor Mrs. Amesbury across the Jordan. And when my own time comes, Lord, please send my own child after me so I won't be afraid and lonesome."

Two nights later she died in her sleep. I returned to the cathedral and thanked the Lord for answering my prayer and giving light once more to poor old Mrs. Amesbury's eyes and mind. I said, "Lord, if I have sent ahead enough mortar and bricks for my mansion in the sky, would You please give it to poor old Mrs. Amesbury? All I shall need is a tiny little place where I can sleep late."

When I fly over Mrs. Amesbury's mansion, I will be glad that I don't have to hunt all over heaven for help to clean up the place. I'll fly back to my little house with one window, pull my rocking chair out onto a cloud, and eat crabmeat and drink Coca-Cola. Every afternoon I'll go down to the Pearly Gates and try my best to persuade old Saint Peter to let in every woman who had to work for a living.

Desperation, despair, and the cruel selfishness of an only child deprived old Mrs. Amesbury of her God-given reason and sense. I went after her clothes and then selected a casket. A hundred times I promised her I would see that she was taken back to Georgia. She had kept up, at great sacrifice, insurance to take her back.

When I got to the undertaker's, lo and behold! whom should I find but the long lost and suddenly found Bertie Jane, whose mind became strangely calm when I assured her that her mother's smidgen insurance policy had been made out to her only child.

Yesterday I took an orchid to Mrs. Amesbury. Its petals clustered under her wrinkled old throat, and the ribbon trailed down across her broken old heart. "My Little Plum, my old and dear friend," I told her, "you are going to God's holy heaven. Bon voyage and cheerio."

A great many righteous churchmen attended the funeral, and the Right Reverend read the words spoken over prince and pauper. And then—wouldn't you know it?—right in the middle of the service, Bertie Jane, looking on her mother's casket for the last time and flayed by remorse, crumpled into a sobbing, quivering heap. The Right Reverend looked at me and nodded, and I left my seat and stepped over a hundred pairs of shoes to get to Bertie Jane's side.

Only God can read the hearts of man and pronounce

judgment, but as I sat there I could not keep these thoughts from my mind: Bertie Jane, the glamorous and beautiful and haughty, had ten hats when her mother was wearing one for ten years; Bertie Jane had her monogrammed note paper when her mother used penny postals; Bertie Jane wore I. Miller shoes when her mother's needed to be resoled; Bertie Jane showed everyone her diamond-studded watch when her mother had never had one to wear.

Some people will tell you that hats, note paper, shoes, and a watch are small things, and I agree. Drops of water are small things, but they make an ocean.

I walked down to the train shed to see that the wooden box was safely on its way. I felt I had kept my promise.

From the adjoining track I heard a voice calling, "Miss Virginia, is that you?" Do you remember a porter named Fred whom your grandfather knew so well? This was Fred's brother, a chef. "Would you like the morning paper, Miss Virginia?" he called from the diner.

I crossed the tracks and reached up for the paper. "Morning paper straight from Virginia," he chortled. At that moment a cloud of steam enveloped me.

The morning paper contained a bundle of bacon. Funny, I thought, how times change. Long ago it was a pillar of fire or a burning bush. Now it's bacon from a cloud of steam. People who don't believe in miracles miss so much. Flapdoodle, trust and obey.

In a last mention of poor old Mrs. Amesbury, let me remind you, my Little Apple, that there are only two living things that you can always depend on to be glad to see you, regardless of what you do or how unmentionable you may become. Those two are your mother and your dog.

Say your prayers.

Love,
Little Mama

Mama Sentimentalizes on the Six Ages of Womanhood

MY LITTLE HONEY BUN:

Thirty years ago this very day you were born. A flower in the window box beside your waiting crib burst into full bloom. I think the heavenly Father offered His blessing and benediction in the form of colored petals.

Yet when I first saw you I wept. I felt deep inside a responsibility for all of the sorrow which everyone who fully lives must at some time come to know.

A mother lives as much by instinct—I call it simply heavenly grace—as by experience or by the books. I could offer you no more understanding and guidance than the Lord provided as my share.

During the five years of infancy my directions were few:

> Don't eat with your fingers.
> Don't leave the yard.
> Say "Thank you" and "If you please."
> Say your prayers.

Then came the ten years of childhood. Do you remember the list of things I tacked on your door?

Study your lessons.
Lower the shades before you undress.
Take your bath.
Brush your hair.
Scrub your teeth.
Cold cream your face.
Say your prayers.

Then followed fifteen years of girlhood when I tried to polish you with the everlasting code of etiquette and conventionality.

Today, my Little Plum, you are no longer a little girl. You are entering twenty years of active womanhood. If I could tack a list to your door today, it would read:

Make a home in which thoughtfulness and kindness reign.
Cultivate friends, remembering that a few will do.
Establish contact and loyalty with your church.
Enjoy every day, remembering that nothing lasts.
Sweeten every situation with a touch of humor.
And as always, say your prayers.

I shall leave you only a widow's mite when my day of rest comes, but you will claim unknown worlds of joy and satisfaction if you are willing to take from me three little words with which the Lord has blessed and preserved me through dark nights and long days: "Trust and obey."

When you reach fifty, I will be gone, but there will inevitably follow for you a fifteen-year period of adjustment, a time to alter your established mode of living and to so arrange your affairs as to procure for yourself sufficient security before you are sixty-five, when wise men say one is old.

After that all you will need or desire will be a little comfort and, God willing, a little kindness.

Happy birthday, Sweetie, and remember always that I love you.

Little Mama

Mama Plays Good Samaritan Along Hospital Halls

MY LITTLE PEACH BLOSSOM:

I perched my gayest bonnet atop my head this morning and wended my way to the hospital to play Good Samaritan in behalf of the Auxiliary at the church.

The ground rules are simple. First you go to the reception desk and scan the cards for names of Episcopalians, and then you drop into their rooms and offer whatever comfort and cheer you can muster, relying on extemporaneous inspiration for the right words.

My modus operandi, however, is somewhat different. If a person is sick or disheartened, what difference does his denominational dogtag make? I have nowhere read that our Lord asked for identification cards before He raised the sick in Galilee or offered the consolations of heaven. Let the Right Reverend tend the flock. I prefer to free-lance.

The hospital halls had that unmistakable sterile atmosphere. The place was so clean it made me sneeze!

The first recipient of my ministrations of mercy was a somewhat disheveled man of forty or so. His hair was in disarray, his face unshaven, and his necktie askew. "Good morning, brother," I said cheerily. "What brings you to these halls of healing?"

He seemed to wince at my gleeful greeting. "I'm a physician from Memphis," he replied, "and I've been in surgery for seven hours. I shall leave these halls of healing just as soon as a taxi comes to take me back to the depot."

I hustled off, thankful that Memphis was willing to share its talent. A little further down the hall was a small sunroom whose only resident at the moment was an old man whose smile as I entered the room was at least a mile wide. A second time I ventured to break the ice with my well-rehearsed greeting: "What brings you to these halls of healing?"

The old man spoke as though he had been waiting a century for someone with whom to speak. "I'm here to have my I.Q. looked after," he confided. He told me that it was low. "I've knowed for some time it had dropped," he added, "but it never hurt me none. I thought I'd better have it looked after. If you please, mam," he said as he held out his hand, suggesting, I presume, that I take his pulse. I picked up a well-worn Gospel of John from a nearby table and tucked it into the brother's shirt pocket.

Sitting in a chair outside a closed door on the second floor was a young girl whose two crying children clutched her shoulders. I knew immediately that soon there would be three crying children. The girl's sobs were heart-wrenching. I cannot remember ever seeing so pitiful a sight.

Surely, I thought, nothing could be as bad as her weeping indicated. Little by little the girl related her story of woe. Not only was her situation as bad as it appeared, but it was far worse. Couldn't have been much blacker.

Her husband, I learned, had been killed in an accident in which their unpaid for and uninsured automobile was demolished. He had lived long enough, however, to run up quite a hospital bill. Now she and her children were miles from home and penniless. She saw no ray of hope or light.

You know, my Little Plum, that my motto has always been that problems are meant to be solved, not prolonged. But what to do?

In a moment a light not of this world began to dawn in my mind. "Your husband," I declared, "can make one last contribution to his family." My words startled me a little, but the girl's face expressed absolute incredibility. She was speechless. Slowly I explained about scientific research and that the authorities in the medical school would exchange her husband's mortal remains for bus tickets back home for her family. Extemporaneous inspiration indeed!

You wouldn't want details of what followed, but I hastened to the office of one of the bigwigs at the medical school who just happens to be on the vestry, and within minutes I had both the papers for the girl to sign and ticket money in my tote bag and also a promise that a check from the cathedral charity fund would be forthcoming.

At the bus depot I waved good-by to the young girl and her children. "Now don't worry," I said. "Just trust and obey. His eye is on the sparrow."

It's time to water the soup. Say your prayers, my Little One.

Love,
Little Mama

P.S. I forgot to ask the girl her denomination.

Mama Attends Sister Annie's Funeral and Meditates Upon Life's Little Lessons

MY LITTLE APPLE:

Annie is dead. A hundred times she said she wanted to live with me until she died. And she did.

Annie's mother hired her out when she was eleven. Now, fifty-eight years later, she has cooked her last dish and scrubbed her last wooden ladle. God rest her soul!

Annie was the most ladylike, the kindest, most patient and unselfish person, black or white, I ever knew.

Yes, my Little One, Annie's gone, and I've closed the dining room in memory.

Yesterday I filled the car with Annie's friends and went to her funeral in a shabby upstairs undertaker's parlor over a store.

The room seemed forlorn. The floor was as bare as life when kindness is gone but as clean as it was bare.

On a little blackboard, near the choir, was written in chalk her name:

SISTER ANNIE

Two preachers officiated because Annie had belonged to two churches and had always adamantly refused to indicate a preference.

The Methodist preacher began the service. His old eyes rolled like those of a tired mule, and his huge stomach rubbed continually against the rough plank pulpit. In an asthma-muffled voice he read God's consoling promise that whosoever believeth shall have everlasting life.

Then he introduced the "heavenly choir" consisting of six half-grown women clad in soiled white muslin and carrying hymnals covered in white paper. They stomped on the floor in a mournful, rhythmic shuffle.

The undertaker rolled the casket in front of the pulpit, placed the "Sister Annie" sign precariously on top, and retired to a squeaky, wobbling bench.

While the heavenly choir sang another spiritual, the pallbearers stood at rigid attention. Each bearer wore a corsage, not a boutonniere, but a corsage consisting of four gardenias and appropriately garnished with a tulle bow. These bearers were Annie's nephews, all born within shouting distance of my grandmother's dooryard.

I noticed old Ross in particular. He and I were born within a few weeks of each other. I remember begging my grandfather to whitewash "little Ross" so we could go to school together.

The elderly preacher asked Annie's family to stand and then for the "white folks" to stand. That meant me. "Are you Miss Virginia?" he asked. I nodded. While I stood he read sonorously a little note I had years before left for Annie when I had visited her in a hospital and had said they should not awaken her to see me. It was a simple and heartfelt expression of gratitude and love for her faithful and loyal friendship. She had placed it under the pillow upon which her dear head rested on the day she died.

After my note had been read, a collection was taken for the family.

The Methodist preacher concluded his portion of the service, and now a Baptist brother moved to the pulpit. As he announced his text, "Be ye ready," he took off his coat, rolled up his sleeves, and clapped his hands. "Now you know," he began, "you have got to be ready if you want a fire in the winter. You know when winter is coming you must get in the coal. That's right. You have got to get it in. Sitting on your cold hands and praying, 'Lord, Lord,' will not fill the bin. The Lord will not build your fire. You have got to get in the coal. That's respectable.

"And you know that hole in the window? You have got to get a rag and chunk it up. You have got to do that. That's respectable. The Lord won't chunk up the holes. He's too busy. You have got to do that yourself. You know your old wicked soul. You have got to get it ready, too.

"Every time you step off the curb you are liable to be killed. When Jesus said, 'Be ye ready,' He was thinking about these very Fords and Chevrolets. He could see them whizzing by in His crystal ball 'way back in Galilee. Now Sister Annie was ready. Praise the Lord!"

Spontaneously and without thinking, I called out "Amen." You would have thought I had gone to camp meetings all my life and not been raised an Episcopalian. A chorus of "Amens" echoed my word, and I felt comforted.

Before the preacher continued, an old woman nearby called out, "Oh, Lord, my poor husband died a sinner!" Then she slumped to the floor. Several of the men began to rub her legs in an effort to bring her to.

After the sinner's widow had been helped to a chair, Sister Maybelle sang Annie's favorite spiritual, "Swing Low, Sweet Chariot." Her voice was a dramatic and exquisite contralto. It was perfectly beautiful. I do believe a tongue of flame came down as at Pentecost. That

song will linger in my memory until the day I too pass over the Jordan.

Then the undertaker cleared his throat self-consciously, tugged a bit on his breeches, and slowly, painfully, lifted the casket lid. The heavenly choir, moving in the same rhythmic shuffle, took their places behind the casket which was rolled up and down each aisle. Every three or four feet the casket was stopped so everyone might gaze upon the tired, placid old face.

I could imagine Annie saying, "Excuse them, Miss Virginia. Some folks haven't any sense." How many times I had heard her speak those very words!

The rambling journey of the casket ended at the doorway. The undertaker literally banged down the lid and bowed to the pallbearers. With much tilting and straining, they bore their burden down the stairs.

In a small burial plot in a cornfield, the wooden box was lowered, and the gravediggers—unceremoniously, I thought—packed the grave with river gravel and cinders. Alternately the preachers besought God to "shackle the devil and save all our souls."

As I stood on that good warm earth, I thought that from every human being we may learn some little lesson to shore our hearts and spirits against the exigencies of daily living. From this humble and lowly woman, I have learned the futility of all striving, the egotism of all pride, and the selfishness of all grief. Consider the lilies . . .

Annie was truly the kindest and most patient person of any race or creed or station I have ever known.

I have tied a ribbon on her cane and hung it in the kitchen, hoping that its sanctifying presence may instill in all who look upon it some small portion of the great qualities she possessed.

Trust and obey.

Love,
Little Mama

Mama Goes to Court—
Twice

My Little Songbird:

Yesterday I had to go to the Court House. They summoned me to grand jury duty. Of all persons, your mother who believes in a second chance for everybody!

Judge Scott was on the bench.

Before I could ask to be released, I had to sit through an assault case. The woman who had brought charges is thirty-five or so and is commonly known as an uncommonly common woman. The "man," chalkwhite with bewilderment and fear, was all of seventeen. Such a mess I have never seen. Sounded for all the world like innocent Joseph in the house of Potiphar.

When recess came, I had my opportunity.

"Will all persons wanting to be excused from jury service stand and state the reason?" called out the bailiff in a bilious voice.

I stood. "Your Honor," I began, "if I had to sit in that jury box for three weeks and listen to the likes of this, I'd fall flat on my face and it would take four strong men to get me up again. So I should be permitted to

35

leave now under my own power."

"Excused," he said. "Bring your summons to the bench."

When I drew near, he straightened his tie self-consciously, raised his eyebrows, and seemed, I thought, to recognize me.

I handed him the summons, but that wasn't all. On the back I had written in pencil: "About the assault case, Judge. How about a ticket back home to his mother for him and for her ninety days in jail for gum chewing in court, streetwalking, and general cussedness?"

This morning I called up Sergeant Jones of the Highway Patrol and asked about the verdict in the assault case. At noon he called back. Jail for the woman for false testimony, and a ticket back to Detroit for the lad. Flapdoodle, trust and obey. I was so pleased I almost stirred the bottom out of the soup kettle!

Did I hear somewhere that the penalty for trying to influence the presiding judge is a heavy fine or imprisonment or both?

Maybe Judge Scott had recognized me, not by name or occasion but because I have a face one can never forget. More years ago than I like to remember I appeared before him when he was sitting in another court.

A man-in-a-hurry sideswiped me on the swinging curve of a narrow high-crowned road. His wheel came off and his big black automobile was badly damaged. Neither of us was hurt, and I returned home thankful for that blessing.

About ten days later a notice came, saying that he was suing me for damages. I would have to go to court. Would my lawyer please reply promptly?

I didn't have an attorney. Didn't need one. Didn't want one. Nothing could convince me to get one. This is the land of the free and the home of the brave. If I had

to go to court, I would be my own lawyer. This man could sue till the cows come home. He had no case and that was that! I would raise my hand, swear to tell nothing but the truth, and simply tell the judge what had happened.

When the day of the trial dawned, my friends made a valiant but unsuccessful attempt to persuade me to get legal counsel. I explained I would handle everything.

On the way to the Court House, I stopped at the dime store and bought two small toy automobiles. Lawyers might shuffle formidable papers in black attaché cases. Two colored toys would satisfactorily serve my purpose.

In court the plaintiff's lawyer talked endlessly. Sound and fury, signifying nothing. When my turn came, I explained that I had been a driver since His Honor was in knee pants and that earlier I had mastered the skills of driving as a most proficient backseat driver.

Questions and explanations followed and then more questions and explanations. At this point I approached the bench, diagramed the curve and crest of the hill with my finger, and placed the toy automobiles on the imaginary line.

The judge studied the toy automobiles for several moments. "Remarkable," he said at last. "Simply remarkable. Case dismissed."

Two weeks later at a church supper, whom should I meet but this very same judge sans judicial robe, sans gavel. "My name is Judge Scott," he said. "The toy automobiles made my little boy very happy."

As I always say, my Little Plum, trust and obey. And remember your prayers.

Love,
Little Mama

Mama Finds Small-time Adventures at the Fair

MY LITTLE HONEY BEE:

Yesterday I went to the Fair, a fertile field for contemplative observation and a ripe grove for plucking small-time adventure. For more years than I like to remember, I have gone to the Fair and always have done what pleased others. This time, being alone, I found upon my arrival that there was nothing I really pleased to do. So I wandered along, expecting something to happen. It always does.

First, I went to the horse-show building and found that a couple hundred mooing, munching cows were competing for the grand championship. The boxes were full, and not wanting to climb the long flight of steps, I just ambled along when suddenly, ka-plunk! a gold-handled cane fell at my feet.

I held it high in the air so the owner might claim it. In a moment he appeared, double criss-cross flannel vest, goatee, and two-toned shoes. He insisted that I come up and sit in his box. The Lord doth provide!

His wife had a bovine countenance and seemed to me

to be happily at home in the surroundings. When the Coca-Cola man came by, my erstwhile benefactor bought me one. His name, he said by way of introduction, was Colonel Clifford Clarkson. This euphonious combination reminded me of the fellow who picked a peck of pickled peppers.

After some time I said: "Colonel, these cows all look alike to me. What constitutes the proper conformation?"

"A prize winner," he explained, "must have a barrel-shaped belly, a flat square rump, and alert ears."

I couldn't have wanted a better clue. I leaned over, nearly pushed him from his chair, and explained in highest glee: "Why, Colonel, you are not talking about a cow. You are describing me!" With that I left, leaving him laughing and slapping both knees and his wife with that same bovine countenance.

Then, hoping for a few minutes of quiet respite, I went to see the waxwork reproduction of "The Last Supper." But, alas, the part in our Lord's wig was crooked, His robe was faded, and He had every evidence of having spent a long and weary day on the dusty roads of Galilee. The tablecloth was wrinkled, the grape juice had a molded scum on it, and the poppy-seed rolls looked as though they had been baked in Vienna in the Seventeen Hundreds.

Two long-faced preachers, wearing rented Prince Albert frocks, stood at the exit and asked in mournful tones, "Have you received spiritual benefit, Sister?" In the tone of an archangel reprimanding a little cherub, I suggested they tidy up the place a bit by ironing the tablecloth and replacing the bread and wine. I didn't mention that the saintly face of Judas Iscariot looked more like a thirty-year veteran Sunday School teacher.

A few feet further was a clown. I just love clowns. Standing next to him was a man who guessed your age. The pitch was routine. You wrote the date of your birth

on a card and handed it to the clown. If the guesser came within three years of your age, you give him fifty cents. If not, he gave you a sweet little bird in a cage.

I knew the man didn't have a chance, so I gave him a half dollar.

On good days I look ten years younger than I am, and on bad days ten years older.

Before making his guess, the man leaned toward the clown who mumbled something inaudible. "Sir," I exclaimed self-righteously, "you are cheating a poor old woman!" He said he wasn't. I said he was. A big red-faced Irishman in the Legionnaire booth nearby jumped over his counter and wanted to know what was going on. Clinging to his lapels, I entreated him to make the man give me my little bird.

The Legionnaire simply took a bird cage from a hook, bowed graciously, and handed it to me, saying, "At your service in war and peace, mam."

My Little Plum, don't let anyone tell you that the age of chivalry has passed!

I rescued a folding chair from a conveniently located bandstand and sat down near the midway to nurse my wounds and to contemplate the joys and miseries which life had stenciled on the faces of passersby.

After awhile a little crowd began to gather around a man holding a mike. I hustled over and found that a local radio station was about to broadcast a quiz game.

After one or two contestants had stumbled over grade-school questions, the announcer pointed to me. My broad-brimmed hat is always an eye-catcher. "What is your name?" he asked.

"Mrs. Crawford." That was the first name that came into my head.

"Where are you from?"

"Louisiana."

"What do you think of our city?"

"I shall withhold comment."

"What brought you to our city?"

"Business interests."

"May I ask what interests?"

"Sorry, classified."

"Now, Mrs. Crawford, for the big prize. Where do the purple starlings go and when?"

"The purple starlings go to Central America in September," I replied in the manner of a well-rehearsed Rally Day pupil.

"Good for you, Mrs. Crawford. You have just won a handsome carving knife."

"Thank you very much."

I'll give the knife to you, Sweetie, on your next visit. Flapdoodle. Just trust and obey.

I was sure by now the Fair had little more excitement to offer. A stone's throw from the exit gate stood a half-blind old woman and a half-starved little boy. He held a cup in one hand and a bell in the other. Some rush of Christian charity had persuaded the authorities to permit these bedraggled folks to seek a meager subsistence at the hands of an easy-spending Fair crowd.

I took the lad to a nearby stand, propped him atop a stool, and ordered milk and a sandwich.

While he contemplated the feast, I returned to the woman and asked if she could sing. She thought she could. "Then start trying and make it loud."

Her words rang out:

> Gabriel, I'm out on a limb,
> Move over, angels, and make more room,
> I'll be joining you in my heavenly home soon,
> Gabriel, I'm out on a limb.

Sensing that the half-blind woman's need was greater than mine, I surrendered to her my folding chair. Then standing with my long, unwrapped carving knife under one arm and the bird cage secure under the other, I rang the bell for all it was worth.

"Keep your dime, Brother, and put in a quarter . . . Thanks."

Several minutes later the sight-seeing bus stopped and a long arm reached from an open window. I took a dollar bill from the extended hand. "Thanks for the crumbs from Dives' table." Then I looked up into the warm, brown eyes of the Bishop!

"Why, Virginia, what on earth are you doing?"

Without thinking I replied, "Just trying to practice what you preach, Right Reverend."

The bus whizzed on, leaving us engulfed in a cloud of exhaust fumes. Suddenly I got the horrible thought that within a week the Bishop will see me when I speak to the state churchwomen. Mercy, mercy!

In the time it took the half-starved boy to eat that sandwich, I collected nearly four dollars. As I left, she said, "You are a good woman." The sweetest words I have ever heard. I gave the boy the bird cage I didn't win, and determined to run for cover. I hadn't gone ten feet when the old woman began again to whine, "Gabriel, I'm out on a limb . . ."

Heavens! who ever said that life is dull?

Honey Bun, remember your prayers.

Love,
Little Mama

Mama Relates the Tale of a Conjured Chest

MY LITTLE PLUM:

I am sending you The Chest, but first I want you to know its incredible story.

God in His infinite wisdom saw fit to "bless" your great-great-great grandmother with a large family of daughters. Your great-great-great grandfather, a harsh Yankee, impressed upon his many daughters the absolute necessity of money.

The oldest daughter, Ellie, was her father's most willing disciple and readily learned the lesson which he considered to be Number One. Having quickly caught his spirit, she trained her ears to detect the sound of jingling coins. She found them in the moneybags of one John Cooley, a Southerner thrice her age. She rubbed his bald old head, and from his pockets rolled all that her heart desired.

Ellie strutted through life with an invisible bluebird perched on her bouncing bustle.

Cotton mills kept the moneybags full.

They lived in a mansion overlooking the willow-fringed river. On either side of the graveled road from the river, imported statues adorned the well-kept lawns. Mythical figures stood amid the holly and magnolias. Cupid, his bow strung, aiming at random. Poseidon sounding his wreathed horn. Athena, tall and dignified, armed for battle, and up to no good. Caper-cutting in cold marble! And all the while Father Zeus looked on in bemused clemency.

Glory be! such splendor you can hardly imagine.

There, tugging against the hawsers, was their own private craft in which they made an annual voyage to New Orleans, returning with a coveted cargo. The plantation hands vied with one another to accompany their master on this trip each year. Permission to go was an open acknowledgment of good service.

All would have been seventh heaven except for The Chest.

This is how the tragic tapestry was woven. My own God-fearing grandmother—God rest her soul!—recited the tale to me while I crouched beneath her sewing machine and turned the wheel whenever her back ached. I would start and stop when her small foot tapped my bare knee. My grandmother—the Lord bless her!—never told a lie, but some dull-witted people, having heard this story, will tell you she never spoke the truth.

John Cooley's father Jacob had a twin named Esau. Esau was a good man, but Jacob was the devil incarnate.

Preparations for Jacob's firstborn included a hand-carved chest made by a slave named, as I recall, Hosea. The finished product did not gratify Jacob's whim, so he administered such a beating to Hosea that the poor old servant died.

In those times the revenge of the slaves always took form in a conjure. To avenge Uncle Hosea's death, they cast a spell on The Chest. Having sprinkled dried owl's

blood inside the drawers, they chanted with appropriate moanings and rhythmic swayings the dirge of conjure and implanted within The Chest an evil power that would bring down The Curse on every owner of The Chest for countless generations.

The Chest was taken from Hosea's workshop to the nursery, but the child for whom it had been made died. This innocent baby was the *first victim* of The Curse.

A brother's child, in whose room The Chest was later placed, was stabbed on his twenty-fifth birthday by his body servant. *Second victim.*

I mentioned that Ellie, Jacob's daughter-in-law, was quick to catch on. She had The Chest put in the attic.

Now while cobwebs encircle its conjured drawers, we must change scenes.

Into the dull and inhospitable drawing rooms of the Jacob Cooley house one day stalked an Irishman, Sean by name, just nineteen and sufficiently witty and handsome to make him less than welcome. When the time of the singing of birds was come and the voice of the turtle was heard, Melinda, the youngest daughter, scarcely sixteen, became hopelessly enamored of him. Sean's rich Irish tenor voice, raised to the accompaniment of Melinda's small fingers on the ivory-keyed spinet, swelled the walls of the English-style house and drowned in a sea of ecstasy the heavy warnings of the fierce-tempered Jacob.

Melinda, who was my own great-grandmother, eloped with Sean. After they left the altar, they had of course no place to go. But Melinda thought of her rich sister Ellie, and the newlywedded couple headed in her direction. She in turn headed them toward one of John's Tennessee farms.

Farm life was lonely and hard. In exchange for the love of a pauper, Melinda was rewarded with a wagonload of babies and a dreary routine of household chores.

The nearest candlelight was many dark miles away.

Melinda wilted under the coarseness of breeding animals and slaughtering them for food. Worms on the tobacco, bugs on the potatoes, ashes on the hearth, fleas under the carpet, chiggers in the grass, ceaseless mooing, bleating, and cackling, and always the fretful, wet-bottomed children. Heavenly days!

Because Melinda enjoyed no beauty save the sunset, Ellie thought she might cheer her sister by sending The Chest. This she did.

By now work had taken all the song out of Sean. Because he was poor, he came to hate all rich men. Because Melinda was shabby, he grew to despise all silken-clad and beribboned women. He determined to do something about their circumstance—in New Orleans.

Hardly had The Chest arrived and Sean departed before Melinda "ailed" and died. She became the *third victim* of The Curse.

Within seven days Sean walked into a lowering stage plank and crushed his head. *Fourth victim.*

The large brood of children were left to be divided up like pups. Ellie, feeling unequal to the ordeal of making a choice, dispatched John to Tennessee. Cooley lined up the children and surveyed them with close scrutiny. The baby Evelyn, aged three, won his heart. The only one of the youngsters to come forward and hold out her hands, she had jet black curly hair, skin as smooth and fine as milk, and the darlingest little arms and legs. Yes, he would make a home for the baby. And that baby, my Little Plum, was none other than my very own grandmother.

John needed a nurse for the child and paid one thousand dollars for Aunty Cherry. I could write reams about her. She was as good a woman as the Lord ever made. She had the faithfulness of black blood, the intelligence of white blood, and the mannerisms of blue blood.

Evelyn now enjoyed every conceivable luxury. In the setting of a rich man's ward, she was a sparkling jewel. Until the day she left his house, at sixteen, she had never brushed her own hair, picked up her own clothes, or washed her own hair.

At sixteen she graduated, having taken what was then called "a teacher's exam" and receiving the highest grade ever accorded "a female." Although only sixteen, she was given full responsibility of a country school.

To prepare herself for her new work, she went into a shoe store to make a purchase. There she met a clerk, a Scotsman named Malcolm Johnson, a small and polite man who was "cute," I thought, even in his old age.

Within eight weeks Malcolm had married Evelyn. A year later she gave birth to my own mother.

I remember Grandma Evelyn as an arrestingly beautiful and magnetically attractive woman who had sad eyes, a quick smile, and more sense in her big toe than all her children had in their heads.

The Chest now came into her possession.

The wedding clothes of Arabella, an orphan who had lived with them, went into The Chest, and soon her young husband died. *Fifth victim.*

The baby clothes of Arabella's child went into The Chest. The child died. *Sixth victim.*

The wedding clothes of Esther, the wife of Evelyn's eldest son, went into The Chest, and she died. *Seventh victim.*

Aunt Sarah hid in The Chest gloves and a scarf she had knitted for her son's Christmas. He fell through a tressle and was killed two days before the celebration of our Lord's birth. *Eighth victim.*

Norah's wedding clothes went into The Chest, and Gardner deserted her. *Ninth victim.*

Ruthie's baby clothes went into The Chest. She was injured and died a cripple. *Tenth victim.*

Meanwhile, Malcolm, a man of parts, walked a road of shining achievement. First he bought a wharf, then a farm, then a coal yard, a lumber mill, a dry goods store, and finally four houses in addition to his own.

When Malcolm died, my grandmother had much wealth, but her heart was as empty as a rain barrel in August. To lessen the memory of her great loss, she moved her duds, including The Chest, from the master bedroom to the guest room. But humiliated by Norah's unwillingness to live at home and heartsick over her son's marriage, she took her own dear life. *Eleventh victim.*

Then The Chest was brought to my house.

Into The Chest went my first child's baby clothes, and he died. *Twelfth victim.*

I put your sister's baby clothes into The Chest, and she was stricken with infantile paralysis. *Thirteenth victim.*

After I put your wedding clothes into The Chest, your first husband died. *Fourteenth victim.*

Stanley Morris put his hunting clothes into The Chest, and he was shot. *Fifteenth victim.*

Robbie put his clothes into The Chest, and within a week he was stabbed through his hand at school. *Sixteenth victim.*

By this time, your God-fearing mother, who holds no truck with four-leaf clovers or broken mirrors or walking under ladders, began to wonder. Were these mere coincidences and nothing more?

I asked poor old Annie if she knew how to break a conjure.

"Oh my, yes!" she exclaimed, her face registering exultant excitement in the anticipation of such a ritual. "First, you got to have a dead owl, one brought to you by a good friend. You can't ask him. He's just got to bring it by one day."

My heart fell flat and hope faded. When would a friend just happen by with a dead owl? Then quite suddenly I remembered the stuffed owl in Tom's room. Johnny Nelson, a good friend, had just brought it by one day!

Then, Annie added, you need a fresh green leaf from a willow tree planted by a good friend. Honey, do you remember funny-looking old Mrs. Mason? Well, she had certainly been my friend, and years ago she planted a willow tree near her doorway over on First Street.

Maybe the tree had long since died or been blown down in a storm. I got into the car and drove hurriedly to her place. Heavens alive! she is long since gone but the tree is now a big one and almost hides the house from view.

"Willows mean sorrow," Annie explained, "and you've got to have one leaf for each curse." I walked into the yard as though I held the mortgage and plucked sixteen large leaves and a couple extra just in case. The astonished tenant looked on in amazement. I nodded courteously to him as I returned to the car.

"Now"—Annie's punctilious directions were punctuated with oh's and ah's—"you got to put the willow leaves into a black pot and boil them from sunup to sundown, at the same time keeping an open eye on the curse-breaking owl." Annie had perched Tom's disheveled owl precariously atop the stove. That vacant-staring owl made me think of Poe's horrible raven and the Ancient Mariner's albatross!

"Now you got to put the liquid in a jug," Annie explained methodically with a wisdom which seemed to flow from some distant fountain, "and bury the jug with its handle to the East 'cause the sun comes from the East and the devil hates light. And you must bury it under a flowering bush because flowers mean love and promise."

Just beyond the kitchen window the heart-shaped lilacs were then in gorgeous bloom.

I followed Annie's directions as carefully as though they were those of a strange recipe from a magazine.

Several days following our curse-breaking ritual, Annie confided that if we were successful in exorcising the evil spirit from The Chest, one of us would surely die when the leaves of the flowering bush dropped.

In September I sadly hung old Annie's cane in the kitchen. Looking through the window, I watched a gust of wind shake the last leaves from the lilac bush. The dry leaves settled gently, playfully, on the ground and covered the spot where the jug still lies.

Some folks will tell you that this is the biggest bunch of lies ever arranged into a bouquet of words. Let them scoff! But don't you doubt your poor old mother, my Little Pet, for what I've told you is Gospel truth.

One day, when I am left alone, I am going to write a book. I'll call it simply *The Chest*, and into it I will put all of the southern lore and doings that I know. Who knows, it might even be published! And, bless me, I want it to make the hair of every single Doubting Thomas and Yankee who reads it stand as straight as a Maypole.

The trials and tribulations of all who have owned The Chest are at an end. Trust and obey, my Dear One, and don't forget your prayers.

Love,
Little Mama

Mama Celebrates a Birthday and Laughs to Keep from Crying

My Little Songbird:

The sweater you sent was a heavenly blessing. Thank Lewis for the precious birthday roses. Tell him I love him more each day, and sometime I'll remember to forgive him for taking my Little Songbird from her cage.

Your sister gave me a box of candy, Mrs. Clements sent some jelly, one of the Auxiliary ladies came with hot homemade bread, Rebekah handed me some country butter in a crock, Mary Anne presented me some fresh chopped pickle, the schoolteachers upstairs had two cases of Coca-Cola delivered, and the Right Reverend phoned to ask if I'd come for dinner. Goody, goody. Trust and obey. The Lord will provide.

Today it is snowing. Ah, beautiful, beautiful winter! Ice, broken hips, pneumonia, frozen feet, frost-bitten ears and fingers, bronchial coughs, quinine and Vicks, and two hundred dollars' worth of coal. Beautiful winter! So invigorating!

Mrs. Bancroft came to call last night. She always tries all of the chairs. She had a bedraggled rose pinned on her hat with a safety pin which was larger than the rose.

I just love Mrs. Bancroft. She is precious. Way up in her seventies and she still sparkles with wit and wisdom —and the joy in living the French call *la joie de vivre*. That's what they call it, but that may not be the way they spell it. Nobody really cares except my old French teacher, and she is gone.

Mrs. Bancroft seemed so pleased when I told her to come back "real soon." Old people have very little attention shown them. Sometimes their lives must seem very dull.

Tomorrow is wash day, and, heaven be praised! I won't have to wash. The laundryman looks so positively beautiful to me on Mondays that I could kiss him.

Did I ever tell you about my friend back home, Tillie Quackenbush by name, whose husband equipped her with a complete laundry? There was something that whirled, something that revolved, something that went up and down, something that rolled sideways, and something that poofed steam. He spent enough on that laundry to keep them comfortable for the balance of their natural lives.

Well, she spent every day shoving things into that horrible monstrosity and yanking them out again. Her arches fell, her back collapsed, her nerves went wild, and her hair stood on end. Throughout her life she had a wet tummy and fiery-red hands. Finally, she tripped over a clothesline and broke four ribs. An operation on her feet cost two hundred, a T-brace for her back cost one hundred and fifty, and X rays and strapped ribs and a month in the hospital cost two hundred and fifty. Later she lifted a tub full of wet clothes and everything went wrong. The surgeon's bill was five hundred.

There's a moral in all this. Someday I must find it.

In another two days I am going out with Lola. She's

come back to sell her house. She's been wearing the most elegant clothes I have seen since the winter of 1912 when I trudged in and out of the White House at the heels of Mrs. Tandanty, she being bespangled, bejeweled, bechained, and bebeaded, and wearing French-heeled slippers, ruffled skirts, and a huge plume over one very, very keen eye.

Before being presented to the wife of the President, the wife of the Vice President, the wife of the Speaker of the House, and the wife of the Jelly Bean, I was always nudged and reminded that "after one's sixteenth birthday, one does not curtsy"!

The neighbors have raised a storm because, six months after her husband's death, she isn't still wearing mourning clothes. Flapdoodle.

Maybe I see Lola differently from other people because I love her. I was with Lola in her Gethsemane, the hospital. I went with her to her Calvary, the graves of her only son and beloved husband. I witnessed Lola's crucifixion when her face was distorted with anguish. I could almost hear the nails being driven through the palms of her hands. When her husband and then the boy, her gallant, handsome, and talented Laddie, were lowered into the yawning earth, I knew that the sharpest sword in all God's creation—a mother's love—had entered her heart.

If it takes red shoes, a red purse, and red flowers on her hat to help her carry on, that's all right with me. And if she wants a night on the town, I still understand.

You know, my Little Plum, not all soldiers are in uniform, and many a hero is never decorated. Life leaves as many scars as battles do.

Lola has been going through Laddie's things, and she looks ten years older. Every day I try to make her laugh. My expert coaching helps a little. I have spent my life

laughing and cutting up to keep from crying. I know it can be done. I have achieved mastery in this necessary art. Laughter for the lips and faith in the heart. There are no other tonics.

Love,
Little Mama

Mama Rejects the Role of Matchmaker

MY LITTLE PEACH:

Cousin Lydia has been home most of the summer, so I have someone with whom to sip a Coca-Cola and to help me with the dishes.

Of course when she returned an army of suitors descended on the place like bees on a honeysuckle bush. But I'd need a train schedule to keep track of their comings and goings.

The dust has begun to settle somewhat. Lydia has given good old Jack the "brush off." He is a decent, clean-minded, proud, polished, sober, ambitious, good-natured, God-fearing aristocrat. At thirty-three he is first-floor buyer in a leading department store. At forty he will have his own.

Lydia wants a man who will sweep her off her feet, a real he-man, she says. I tell her that when Jack's wife is perfumed and rested and on her way in a shiny car to the club, she will be hanging out four thousand diapers and her dishes will be stacked from the sink to the ceiling. Her so-called he-man will be lounging on a ragged old Chesterfield, he'll have four-days' whiskers on his chin, and he'll have a dime in his pocket.

I'm having no more luck as a matchmaker with Lydia than I had, my Little Dove, with you.

I don't guess I will ever see Jack again. I just love him. But as Lydia says, he's not a real he-man and doesn't believe in kissing before proposing.

Edgar Sylvester, one of the Sylvesters, called me up last night and said he would like to meet your cousin. Heavenly bells! I almost dropped the telephone. He is a bachelor who won't see forty again, a vestryman at the cathedral, and is a director of six or eight companies. Trust and obey. Maybe I won't have to go to the poorhouse after all.

Remember when Lydia was at school and the drooling little Ronald C. Sylvester III was being bawled out for never knowing anything? There he stood in tears before the class, an object of shame and derision. What did Lydia do? She rushed from her seat, put her arms about him, and said that the reason she loved him was because he didn't have any sense.

Coming from the store this morning, I passed old Mrs. Granger's place. The most beautiful roses were protruding through the picket fence. "I'm lonely," one particularly beautiful rosebud pleaded. "Please take me to your home." I really didn't want it. The devil made me steal it. Somehow I think the Lord understands why I didn't feel sorry. After all, didn't He pull somebody's corn? And on the Sabbath, too.

The two teachers on the second floor are going away for the weekend. They know where there is a country ham. Yum, yum! Trust and obey.

Since Annie crossed the Jordan River I have lost twenty pounds. Nobody knows it but the scales and me, and nobody would believe it if I told them! If I could just figure out some form of exercise that would include

every single muscle while I stood in one place, maybe I could really lose weight. I know, I'll stop at the cathedral and light a candle to Saint Vitus.

At the market this morning there was a line of customers reaching out to the curb. The manager came to the door and announced sourly, "Expectant mothers come to the front of the line."

A young woman next to me obviously qualified. As she left she said, "Come on." In a moment it occurred to me what she meant, and I followed my benefactor to the counter. Flapdoodle, trust and obey.

Now after all, my Little One whom I have taught never to compromise with the truth, I am a "mother" and I am "expectant," because anytime, any day, anywhere I am expecting anything. If that doesn't qualify me, what would?

Tell Lewis I will most certainly make some beaten biscuits when you and he come. I hope he can eat them.

The other day I tried to make salt-rising bread. It foamed up and hissed at me. Then it collapsed like a punctured balloon. I put it in the garbage can and hid it under corn shucks.

Into the kitchen stomped Mr. Milton, a gent who stays in the corner room upstairs and smokes a horrible-smelling Sherlock Holmes pipe. "Don't I smell dough?" he asked, smacking his lips.

"Dough?" I said. "Oh, that's my new Wilderness Madness perfume."

Rebekah, who was sitting on a stool at the sink where she had been placidly contemplating a peck of unpeeled potatoes for twenty minutes, broke out into a spasm of laughter. In a few moments she allowed that it was the pepper she hadn't been using.

Notes from Mama's Unwritten Notebook: Get some gold stars at the dime store. Good-sized ones. Paste them on the ceiling in the northeast corner of your porch. Arrange in the shape of the Big Dipper. Seven stars in all. They will show through the door when you are in your living room. Some smaller stars here and there might be cute. Perhaps this doesn't appeal to you. Just an idea.

Remember your prayers.

Love,
Little Mama

Mama Reminisces

on

Washington
Peters

MY LITTLE CHICKADEE:

Five days ago Washington Peters dropped dead, without insurance and without a friend in sight.

His weary bones were headed for the potter's field.

I found him on a cooling board in an undertaker's ramshackle warehouse. A pot-black sheet covered his body except for his old white head. A cold hand, toughened by hard work, hung limp.

As I have told you a million times, Wash was a favorite of mine. Never has anything affected me so hopelessly as seeing him there, alone and abandoned.

Wash fought in the first war. He deserved the dignity of a soldier's grave. I wired D.C., and they sent funeral costs and their permit for his burial in the Zachary Taylor Cemetery.

His grave is near the flagpole. The undertaker gave me the flag that covered his coffin. I've had a pall of poinsettias put on the fresh earth.

Afterward I went down to the station to see that his one sister got the money taken from his pay every month. The Pullman porters, freight laborers, and dining-car chefs lined up to shake hands with me.

His boss, a Mr. Rogers, had gotten after Wash for not having any insurance. He told him he wasn't worried 'cause when he died he knew "Little Miss" would come and get him.

I am left now with only Mary Anne, Sadie, and Rebekah. When these three links are gone, I will have to transplant myself, or try to, to the strange thinking and, to me, the selfish indifference of a younger generation.

Now I must be off to the kitchen and the same old pot and pan and skillet and roaster. And I will say to the pot, "Gone is Washington, my houseman, thirty-five years of perfect service, able chauffeur, and most originally amazing butler."

Then I will say to the pan, "Gone is Aunt Jane, the nursemaid, with her corncob pipe and old-time lullabies."

Then I will say to the skillet, "Gone is Martha, my mother's personal maid and my haven in time of storm."

To the roaster I will say, "Gone is Annie, the cook, last reminder of former elegance and private-car days."

And I will hum the words, "Gone are the days when my heart was young and gay . . ."

Gone is my silken cushion, and I find myself seated on a tack.

And what has that to do with this night and this meal? I will rightabout-face and say to myself: "Cheerio, you can't relive the past. Get going, and thank the good Lord you have a pot, a pan, a skillet, a roaster, and something to put in them."

I, an animate old fossil of better days, find myself at last in the kitchen alone. Do I feel sorry for myself? Heavens, no! I sweat and I stir and I beat, mash, and grind, and supper is ready at six. Flapdoodle, trust and obey. The Lord doth provide!

But Wash will always lie closest to my heart. You, my Honey Bun, will think of him only as someone who lifted you from the train steps into a shining car, who always kept the pitchers filled with water and the fire logs in neat rows. But Wash was more than that to me.

It was Wash who took me to school, taught me to curry a horse, to brush out its tail, to adjust a martingale, to judge the length of a check rein and the snugness of a saddle girth, to handle both reins with one hand so I would have the other free for the whip.

66

Wash taught me to pick a chicken and bathe a dog. It was Wash's admonishing me "to aim true for a weak spot and then swing with all your might" that enabled me forty years later to send a burglar fleeing from the house.

It was Wash who spanked me soundly when I turned the hose on my mother's prissy callers.

It was Wash who helped me to get my clothes out of the house when I eloped at sixteen. Wash's were the sympathetic arms into which I sank, overcome with indignant wrath and youthful heartbreak after my humiliating arrest and forcible return.

Yes, Wash was a favorite. God rest his soul.

Remember your prayers. His eye is on the sparrow.

Love,
Little Mama

Mama Writes of Life and Love in a Rooming House

My Little Honey Bun:

Your old mother's boardinghouse has become the house of romance once more. The porch stairs are a golden carpet leading to the stars. The spacious living room is a sylvan pool from whose bank the young lovers cast pebbles and count concentric circles. In the dining room only nectar and ambrosia are served.

I have four teachers rooming here now. You've met Dolly and Edith. The others came in September. Each has a beau, and one by my last count has three.

The same old handholding and whispering has started up in the kitchen and on the front porch. Heavenly days!

Do you remember the sign I put up in the kitchen?

MAMA DON'T 'LOW NO KISSIN' IN HERE

Sammy Parker wrote under it in lipstick:

WE DON'T CARE WHAT MAMA DON'T 'LOW
WE GONNA KISS HERE ANYHOW

Sammy took one of my boarders to the altar, exchanged

68

sweet words for a sixty-hour week and a mortgaged home, and fills a pew each Sunday with his offspring. And that, my Little One, is the story of and the glory of love.

One of the sweetest human beings I've ever known, by name Viola, who asked for a room after she signed to teach at the school, has been courted by an aged man of thirty-seven. The poor fellow wanted a home, a cook, a housekeeper, and a comforter. But his technique was all wrong. The more he brought chocolates and diamonds and flowers, insisting that she say yes and urging that she set a date with the preacher, the more furious she became. He might have been surprised at the progress he would have made if he had taken it slow and easy. He let his clutch out too fast and killed his motor. I don't expect to see him any more, and we won't have his b-e-a-u-t-i-f-u-l roses in the parlor.

And then there's Mr. Matthews. His remarkable resemblance to Don Ameche has given me a thrill every day since he took a room here three years ago. Tomorrow is his wedding day, and I shall lose my last Presbyterian. All day long he has been upstairs scraping, banging, stacking clothes, and hunting up the other girls' letters for the furnace.

Rebekah came into my room and whispered, "Pretty, is Mr. Matthews *really* leaving?" Then she stopped by his door to wish "you and Mrs. Matthews a mighty sweet time and all that." And wouldn't you know it? She added, "I know Pretty is sure going to miss your eight dollars."

I've already rented Mr. Matthews' room. I didn't advertise. Just waited for the Lord to send me somebody. Fourteen men came by and whom did I settle on? A pink-and-white old bachelor who quotes Shakespeare, hates women—"You excepted, mam"—and radios, and can't stand noise. I've got just the place for him what with all the roomers, Rebekah's chortling country melodies in the kitchen, eleven radios, and the Right Reverend's voice booming on the porch whenever he passes by.

Dolly is so cute. Every few days she comes into the kitchen toting a basket of Coca-Cola which she gets at wholesale prices. And Edith has actually volunteered twice to wash dishes. The other night they scratched my

back and I felt like a kitten. Flapdoodle, my Dear, just trust and obey.

One more tidbit from Virginia's Southern Manor! Last night there came to my much-frequented door a small man in a very expensive suit. Did I know him? Couldn't say as I did. One of the dozens of soldiers whom I fed now comes back to say hello. His missions over Germany enthralled your brother.

I enjoyed his quiet merriment and was fascinated by his ghostlike tread and sudden appearances.

He came for dinner and stayed for breakfast. While his fourth cup of coffee cooled, he went to the phone, ordered from New York his plane to be in readiness to take him to Brazil, showed me his FBI badge, kissed me on both cheeks, and was gone before the coffee was cold. Heigh-ho, Silver! He is a counterspy. Don't you just love that?

Say your prayers and don't forget your

Loving Mama

P.S. Mr. Matthews always sleeps on top of his cover and I've never had to change his sheets. Now that blessing has gone forever.

Mama Preaches at the Goodwill Chapel During an Epidemic of Episcopalians

MY LITTLE MAGNOLIA BLOSSOM:

The green grass is brightening up a bit after having been asleep so long under the snow. Today I am going to rake the ugly old rubbish out of it so it can grow. I'm sure the grass will think that feels good. Like having your back scratched.

At a church council meeting some weeks ago I was asked to be the Episcopal representative to the Goodwill Chapel for Lent. I soon learned that my responsibilities meant the whole shebang including preaching on Ash Wednesday and Good Friday.

The Right Reverend was dee-lighted and immediately promised the help of at least ten rectors. Two other women from the cathedral promptly assured the meeting that the Auxiliary would assist in any way.

These people at the chapel are a forlorn folk who must at times feel that God has forgotten them. Our work is simple: to bring spiritual encouragement and as-surance to them.

At the council meeting one woman—a Methodist or

Baptist, I don't remember which—rose to her feet, expressed herself as being greatly troubled, and asked if I intended to make the hour-long Good Friday service denominational. My Little Plum, my face flushed and I felt my hair rise. I was glad I was wearing my hat with the broad brim.

I stood up, feeling for a moment that I was on trial for my life. "What do I intend to say?" I began. "A Hudson was the Bishop of London, and a Cary laid the cornerstone of William and Mary and was its first rector. I shall speak words they loved and cherished, words which the forefathers of everyone present here this evening loved and cherished.

"During the first fifteen minutes I will review the only four questions to be asked us by Jesus at the Last Judgment.

"Then for fifteen minutes I will tell those poor neglected men that the price of their redemption was the blood that flowed from Calvary, and that salvation is obtainable through repentance, everlastingly established by the forgiveness of God.

"The third fifteen minutes will be on the last hour of our Lord on the Cross and the three figures at the foot of the Cross: the Saviour's Mother, Mary of Magdala, and John. They represent the trinity of Christian doctrine which are love, forgiveness, and service.

"Then will follow the prayers written by the Apostles long before so-called Christians in their zeal and stupidity frustrated the purposes of the Almighty by fragmentation and denominational talk."

The good woman who had been troubled allowed that her mind had been put to rest!

This is the first time that the Goodwill Chapel has had an epidemic of Episcopalians. Only one member of the Auxiliary turned me down when I asked for help. She said she would have to wash her hands of the whole thing. That seemed a singularly appropriate figure of speech for Holy Week!

Later the Goodwill Chapel phoned to ask if I would fill the chapel pulpit on Monday of Holy Week when only those of the Jewish faith would be attending. Some benighted people consider them to be outcasts and unenlightened.

Maybe you are wondering what I said on that occasion. Like you, my own daughter, I am never at a loss.

I began by praising the universal charity of Catholics and tearing to shreds the unimportant opinions of some Protestants which divide and defeat.

I said that to the Hebrew people all mankind owes the Bible and our knowledge of the one true God men call Jehovah. I reminded them that God saw fit to select the Messiah from this chosen people. From among them came the only two sinless beings who ever walked the earth, Jesus and His mother. From among the Jews came the colossal faith sufficient to raise the dead. Judaism, I said, is the cradle of Christianity, and the founders of Christianity were all Jews. At the Transfiguration the faces of Jews—Moses and Elijah—looked down upon their holy Kinsman when the heavens were opened. The Jews had carried the torch of faith down through the ages through pestilence, famine, world deluge, slavery, and bondage. Etc., etc.

I concluded by saying that no religion deserves the scorn of another and that those who scorn represent the antichrist because scorn has no place in Christ's teachings.

When I saw handkerchiefs begin to come out and bearded men wipe their eyes, I felt like apologizing for all the unkind words which have separated God's children. When the men formed in line to pump my arm and tell me they were glad they had come, I knew my

words had not been spoken in vain. The blind man at the piano, his cheeks wet with tears, said he had not felt so glad since he said his prayers at his mother's knee. And the superintendent of the Chapel said, "The la-de-da words of some of the robed preachers do not go over down here. These are simple and plain people who want a simple truth."

"I am a simple woman," I replied, "and I cannot speak with the tongues of men and of angels."

When I stepped into the warm street, a shabbily dressed old man pressed into the palm of my hand a mezuzah, scarcely an inch in length, and without speaking a word hurried away.

I have put this mezuzah among my papers with Aunt Gertrude's rosary. When the Lord comes for me, I want you to put the rosary in one hand and the mezuzah in the other. I trust the holy cross will be stenciled on my heart. I want these three symbols to testify to the Father that I have loved all of His children.

Tomorrow, my Little Plum, we celebrate the resurrection of our Lord. I shall wear the gayest bonnet I could find in six stores to represent my cheerful heart.

Love,
Little Mama

Mama Remembers Annie and Witnesses a Strange Wedding

My Little Chickadee:

My new roomer's beau is back for the weekend. La-de-la! I am putting a bowl of fruit in the sunroom so she can chew on them and not eat him entirely up.

Annie has been gone twenty months yesterday. God bless her soul! She rests on Abraham's bosom. No, I expect she is not really resting. I believe that in that temple not made with hands she has some important assignment. Chief cheer-er-upper. The place she has left in my heart could not be filled by the moon and all the planets. My lines have fallen in pleasant places—in green pastures and beside still waters. I was not prepared for the Gethsemane of her passing.

The Right Reverend said that time would help me to forget, and I said, "I don't want to forget. I want only a larger memory—big enough for all whom I've loved and lost awhile. I pray, 'Dear God, keep their memory bright and beautiful—and exciting.'"

Down home on the family plot is a stone bench on which is inscribed these words:

TO LIVE IN HEARTS WE LEAVE BEHIND IS NOT TO DIE

But I have indulged myself too much. Annie used to

77

say, "Haul down the flag! This is Lugubrious Day for Miss Virginia."

A very excited neighbor, "hallelujah" written from ear to ear, fluttered across the worn doorsill and called, "Look what I've got." She waved a fifty-dollar bill in the air and promised that I could join her in the Promised Land. She had just rented her wee bedroom out for Derby weekend. No trouble a-tall! People were very nice. Etc., etc. All you do is register your room with the AAA or one of the agencies connected with housing for Derby weekend. After all, the hotels require that you take a room for the entire weekend. One night would not do. A rooming house was a land flowing with milk and honey. My neighbor's idea was as contagious as measles.

The family could crowd into my room for the weekend and that would leave two bedrooms for the Suppliants of the Turf. And what would I do with the green manna? Why, take a trip, of course.

But before I reached for the road maps, I grabbed the phone and while my hallelujah neighbor dictated what I was to say, I talked with one of the agencies. "I want only the most respectable . . . Yes, two bedrooms with bath between . . . Yes, middle-aged paying guests . . . Colonel Timothy . . . Yes, I've got the name . . . And Mrs. Rector . . . Thanks."

They would arrive on Thursday, remain through the "run for the roses," and leave Sunday morning.

The rooms were scrubbed and brightened, and everything that was cumbersome was swept across the hall into my bedroom.

On Thursday I was sick. Rebekah called my doctor. While I lay moaning and groaning on the couch in the living room, Rebekah answered the doorbell. A lovely-looking woman of fifty or so entered. She was beautifully dressed. The taxi driver set her handsome luggage in the hallway.

I heard her inform Rebekah that she was Mrs. Rector, our Derby guest, and would like to see her room. First, Rebekah brought her to me, and while we conversed Rebekah trudged up the stairs to check on the room.

When Rebekah returned, the guest was gone. "Heavens! Where is she?" exclaimed Rebekah in dumfounded bewilderment.

I slowly explained that when the doctor entered the door, Mrs. Rector rushed to him and there followed such hugging and kissing as you hadn't seen since the days of Cleopatra. The flabbergasted doctor fled through the door and Mrs. Rector followed in hot pursuit.

What to do? Call another physician? The more I thought about it the less pain I felt, and I decided I didn't need a doctor after all.

In a few minutes Mrs. Rector burst through the front door. She was in tears, distress was written all over her quivering body, and her heart was forever broken. She slumped into a chair next to me and sobbed, "Oh, have you ever been jilted?"

No, I admitted, but everything else has happened to me. To take her mind from her sorrow and to clear the mystery which beclouded mine, I asked, "How long have you known Doctor Bullock?"

"Doctor Bullock?" Mrs. Rector cried. "Who is he? I don't know any Doctor Bullock."

My mouth flew open and I could have swallowed the sun, moon, and stars. "Doctor Bullock was the man you just consumed with hugs and kisses."

"Oh," she fairly shouted, "I thought he was Colonel Timothy!" Her face lighted up like opening night at a supermarket. No sun was ever as bright as her beaming smile. Then her story unfolded.

She and a Colonel Timothy had been corresponding through a matrimonial agency. Their mutual decision was to meet at Derby time and if all went well to be married. Merciful heavens!

The bride-to-be made an instantaneous recovery, and I phoned Doctor Bullock to explain the unusual circumstances. Never had he been so glad to receive a phone call. This woman, he said, had pushed him through the door, insisting that they hurry someplace for luncheon. He had retreated to his car and driven away as quickly as possible.

In time the bridegroom came. You could smell him before you saw him, for he was drenched in lily-of-the-valley perfume. A large wart on his nose was covered with talcum. His manner was gentlemanly and reserved. I introduced him to Mrs. Rector who extended her hand coyly. I had to do most of the talking.

I left them to search their hearts on the sofa.

The following evening they confided their decision to marry, asking if they might be permitted to be married "at home," meaning in my house. And did I know a preacher who might come? "Yes," I said, "preachers are pretty lonely on Derby weekend, and I'll find one."

I called people from far and near to attend the ceremony. For the reception we had cake and punch.

After the reception, the groom went to his room and locked the door. He snored till these sturdy brick walls shook.

I sat up and talked with the blushing bride most of the night. About 2 A.M. we called her children long distance. I rang our old dinner bell into the receiver of the phone so that the relatives might know of the festivities.

On Sunday morning he paid his bill and she paid hers. Then they left. A few days later a delivery boy brought me a wonderful sun lamp. Something I've always wanted. Just trust and obey.

Love,
Little Mama

Mama Recalls Buffalo Bill and Lists Ten Commandments for a Happy Marriage

MY LITTLE BLUEBIRD:

Billy Ferguson has just come in. His breeches are in tatters from football, and a huge knife hangs from his belt. "Miss Virginny," he yelled, "can I borrow your fiddle? I want to play 'Turkey in the Straw.'"

"By all means," I said. "It is a beautiful day to fiddle and just the right time of year to be thinking about turkey."

He is now seated on the front porch, and the air is rent with horrible screeches.

By the way, the railroad people have just sold your grandfather's private car to a circus. Good old Number 100. The ancient wheels will click over the rails once more.

My dear mother—God rest her soul!—will smile in her grave. She simply adored a circus. Never missed one.

My earliest recollection is that of being lifted up and held in the arms of the white buckskinned, fringe-clad Buffalo Bill. Any old-timer will tell you that William Frederick Cody was a very handsome man.

Now I have two dollars in the bank, one thousand unpaid bills, and a half-clean house. I think I will call my creditors and ask them to release me from my indebtedness because Buffalo Bill once cuddled me in his arms.

Nannette has finally set the date for her marriage to C.B., and I'm planning a shower as an appreciative gesture for two years of superb back-scratching.

How do you like my party invitations which I've sent to twenty-four mutual friends?

THE PLEASURE OF YOUR COMPANY
IS REQUESTED AT A
GOOD ADVICE SHOWER
FOR NANNETTE AND C.B.
Each couple is asked to please submit
"Ten Commandments for a Happy Marriage."
Write on the enclosed sheets and return
promptly so the sheets may be secured
in a scrapbook and presented to the
bride and groom for safekeeping and
future perusal.
Prizes for the best advice.
Judging by couples longest married.

I have already written my "Ten Commandments." What do you think of them?

To the Bride
1. *Flatter him. Every man wants his wife to consider him an Adonis.*
2. *Feed him. The best way to a man's heart is still through his stomach.*
3. *Keep the house in order. A man's home is his castle.*
4. *Make him think what you want was first his idea.*
5. *Treat his mother as you want yours treated.*

To the Groom
1. *Tell her often that she is beautiful. Time will make you a convincing liar.*

83

2. Tell her often that you love her. She may always doubt you.
3. Don't begin an argument. You can't win it.
4. Don't tell her that her relatives are horrible. She knows it.
5. When all the bills are paid, divide what is left with her so she may have the little atrocities for which she longs.

Benny Benson, a second-year medic who has been in the second-floor green room since September, came down last night to have a course summary typed. His grades are superb, but I had to tell him how to spell the words he so fluently dictated. His enunciation, vocabulary, and verbalization are perfect. His spelling is zero.

I who have not been in school for a century must tell him how to spell medical words.

When he asked how come I knew these words, I said: "After having rented rooms for years, I know all about *physiognomy*. As blue as I have sometimes been, naturally I know *lymphocystosis*."

When it comes to *pestiferous*, what a paper I could prepare for him about pests and their cause and effect!

Poor little medical student, how much he has to learn.

Billy and the fiddle are still at it. Not long ago he screamed for me. I thought the house was on fire. He wanted to know if he could stuff a cat in my basement. He had just received his mail-order correspondence course diploma in embalming. Well, blow me down! "Don't tell me, Billy, that you are going to be an undertaker!"

"Oh, no, Miss Virginny, I'm not going to stuff anybody. Only a cat."

Twenty minutes later I heard such a noise as only a cat can make. A distinct and unmistakable feline disturbance.

Then before long Mrs. Shepardson called up. You know Mrs. Shepardson. Everyone does! She thought she had heard a rifle shot in my backyard. She had? Dear me, such strange noises the wind makes in these big trees this time of year. "And how are you, Mrs. Shepardson, and how is your family?" It enrages her to ask about her family what with a daughter married to a traveling man who doesn't support her and a son married to a girl she's never met.

And so your mother whiles away her days busy at little commotions—tidal waves in a fish bowl.

Love,
Little Mama

P.S. Don't show this letter to Lewis. He already knows that his mother-in-law is a wild woman.

Mama Eases Into Grandmotherhood

MY LITTLE SWEETIE:

My cup runneth over. I know millions of women have become grandmothers, and the role for one is not different from that of all the others. Yet I feel as though I am the world's first grandmother and that no other woman ever felt or could feel as I do.

Motherhood for you will be a burden. Fatherhood for Lewis will be a responsibility. Grandmotherhood for me will be an undiluted joy. Praise God from whom all blessings flow!

Before I left your side at the hospital and took my long, lone journey back to Louisville, I told you I would send something mighty precious for little Beverly. It is her baby cup and has been held in the tiny hands of her mother, grandmother, and great-grandmother.

On its side I have had engraved this little prayer:

> To Beverly
> God grant that you
> may grow
> in spiritual grace.

Of course you have a thousand questions. Every grandmother has a thousand answers. You have asked me to jot down whatever wisdom time has given to me, and this I do, knowing my wisdom must give way to your own understandings.

What I write is far ahead, but I may be gone to glory when the time comes.

No matter how little Beverly is raised, you will find, when she is grown, that you should have done differently.

As you have heard me say, but likely have forgotten, your sister was so weak she had to be assisted in swallowing by massaging the sides of her throat. Forcing a normal child to swallow creates fear.

When God puts teeth in a baby's mouth, it is time to eat. Even one tooth is a signal to begin. All food before then should be in liquid form.

I taught you to swallow with sugar and peppermint candy. I would moisten my fingertip, dip it in sugar, and let you taste. You liked it and would swallow involuntarily.

Then I let you suck on a peppermint stick. Peppermint is stomach toning and aids digestion. When your mouth was full of sweet saliva, you swallowed.

Then I alternated very soft food with the peppermint stick. Bulky feeding crowds a child's throat and frightens or chokes it.

The first feedings should be thinned until they have, in the mouth, almost the same feel as liquid.

And for heaven's sake, remember that at any age a child should never be scolded at the table.

When Beverly begins to eat, let her eat in any way she

will just as long as she eats. When she is about two and a half, and fully understands what you say, sit her down, not at meal time but at tea-party time when you are alone with her, and teach her what you expect her to do at the table.

Do you remember the little dishes you and your sister

had? They did the trick. Don't think one or two lessons will suffice. It will take until little Beverly is of school age.

Manners in children are a matter of habit only. A habit formed at a tea table opposite a doll will be continued at your own and other people's tables.

You can't put this bunk over on a boy. He would knock the doll out of the chair, turn over the table, and ride it for a horse.

All children are born savages. Example civilizes them and only pride makes them conventional. They are born selfish or unselfish, cruel or kind, smart or stupid, honest or dishonest. Good influences bring out the good in them. Respect and affection you cannot command. Having been earned or deserved, they are the reward of your own merit.

When your children are little, you are a wonderful person. When they reach their teens, you become a mean old thing who doesn't understand anything. When they are in their twenties, you are old-fashioned and meddlesome. Only by leaving home can they be happy. By the time they are thirty, mother suddenly becomes real smart. Funny how much mother learned so quickly! When they are forty, you are usually gone, and they will wish to highest heaven that they had known all along just how much you could have helped them if they had let you.

I hope you and Lewis will bring little Beverly to see me real soon. Won't you try?

More than all else I anticipate the day when Beverly will speak her first word. Your sister's first word was *pretty*, and she still loves pretty things. Your brother's was *light*, and the outdoors has always fascinated him. Yours was *pie*, and I dare say good food is your specialty. The first word I ever said was *sky*. I still love to look up. I see crooked chimneys and dead limbs and sagging wires that other people never see. And higher still I have always hoped to see the gracious abundance and all-encompassing love of Infinity.

Love,
Little Mama

Mama Finds a Philosopher in Her Backyard and Celebrates a Domestic Sacrament

My Little Plum:

The other day a sixteen- or seventeen-year-old boy suddenly appeared at the door and announced that he had come to chop some fire logs. I had never seen him before, but I reckoned that his coming was an answer to a prayer I hadn't had time to offer.

I heard a half-dozen whacks. Then no more. Such silence that you could hear it. In a moment there was a knock at the screen. "Lady," he said, "I can't chop no more firewood."

"And why?"

"Well," he replied, squirming under the weight of the ax, "I must allow as I'm not in exactly the right mood."

"Come now," I reasoned, "don't you know that Abraham Lincoln chopped wood?"

"Yes, mam, but he wanted to be President, and I don't!"

I had found a philosopher in my own backyard. More rare these days than a bluebird.

The sun felt warm on my back, the locusts were singing, and the air was full of the fragrant smoke of burning leaves. Who could capture the right mood to chop wood on such a day?

The boy wilted under my gaze of perfect understanding which he thought was a look of reproach.

"You know," I told him, "there is a big show at the Palace. Brass band, singing, and all the rest. How would you like to go? The show starts in twenty minutes."

His lips tightened into such a smile as one sees only once in ten years. "Oh, Lady, you wouldn't be fooling me?" he pleaded.

"Absolutely not," I assured him, adding confidentially, "though I did steal a rosebud once, I definitely wouldn't fool you. Quick now," I said, "ten cents for carfare for putting the ax back in the basement and money for the show for not wanting to be like Abraham Lincoln."

"Whoopee," he called, making for the back fence and clearing it like a gazelle.

And the firewood? The Lord will send me an old humdrum from whose soul all poetry has fled, and there will be firewood when I am dead and gone.

I think I will have gas logs put in my fireplace and get rid of all my ashes.

Today is annual fall-cleaning day, which has become a ritual by now. A domestic sacrament.

The high priest is Rebekah, who has been with me for more than thirty years now. She is just an old-timey country gal who could not change trains in a big station if her life depended on it. I send her to the drugstore for a little diversion, but she stands on the corner—stands and stands and stands—"waiting for everything to get by." She doesn't trust the lights because they are "too changeable." She's the kind that wakes you up and asks if you are asleep. But she is as good as gold and she's an inspiration and spiritual tonic to have in the house.

Never a day passes that she doesn't ask after you and "Mr. Lewis, too."

Rebekah's daughter is cut from a different cloth. She knows how to get there and back. Left the country in her teens and has the get-up-and-go city life gives you.

Age has taken its toll of Rebekah. She just informed me that no man is what he is *cranked* up to be. Flourishing a dust rag, she sits in a corner of the dining room when company comes. "Getting ideas," she explains, for her "vocabuborum." Don't you love those last three syllables—"u-bore-em"?

Rebekah and her daughter were here bright and early. Soon another house girl made her appearance and then three yardmen.

Rebekah sat on her throne in the kitchen and quickly dispatched each of her vassals to his respective post.

My mop boy laments that he is "too busy to work, too poor to quit, and too young for the government to support him." He thinks he can "do better" and his wages "don't excite him."

Rebekah has been on the phone off and on all day, calling country kin and hoping "Mr. Bell's wires will help me get an extra hand or two."

Her telephone eloquence makes one wonder if the three R's are all we've been told. She never went to school, but I've known many a man at the University who cannot handle the English tongue as easefully. Here are some snatches of her purple speech:

"Hello, Sarie . . . Sure it's me. Nobody else . . . Oh, I'm just sitting here and blowing myself out . . . No, I've done no hard work. Pretty"—that's me—"won't let me no more. She's got folks running everywheres with buckets. Never seen so much soapsuds in all my days. You'd think it was Spring the way Pretty's sap is rising! . . .

"Now, Sarie, you sound wearisome. What's clouded

you up so? . . .

"Joe is the promptingness man for his meals. That man is ready for supper before breakfast is started . . .

"Me and Pretty been talking this morning about the time when she was ten years old. Surely was one bad child . . . That's right. She's not changed a little bit. Not at all, except she's got higher and wider . . .

"When Pretty was a young maiden lady and her children were babies, she carried on bad enough about cleaning, but, oh my heavens, she's taken a post-mortem study in it . . .

"Now, Pretty, I tell her, if you don't quit that short-circuit sparking, you'll have nary a fuse left . . . But she's not one to have her private spice stirred into . . . Sometimes no one knows what she says, but we always know what she means . . .

"Well, the day is going home, and so will we so as day can leave again . . . Good-by, watch out, and bear down on your praying, my pastor says."

Five barrels of trash are now lined up at the garden gate. How one woman's house can accumulate so much I'll never know! Much of it is the duds the roomers left behind. I think the house must be haunted by mementos of old loves, old hopes, and old dreams.

I think I'll beg the Right Reverend to put back in the prayer book the words:

> From ghosties and ghoulies
> And long-legged beasties
> And things that go bump in the night,
> Good Lord, preserve us!

Love,
Little Mama

Here's what kids and grown-ups have to say about the Magic Tree House® books:

"Oh, man . . . the Magic Tree House series
is really exciting!"
—Christina

"I like the Magic Tree House series. I stay up
all night reading them. Even on school nights!"
—Peter

"Jack and Annie have opened a door to a world
of literacy that I know will continue throughout
the lives of my students."
—Deborah H.

"As a librarian, I have seen many happy young
readers coming into the library to check out
the next Magic Tree House book in the series."
—Lynne H.

Magic Tree House®

For a list of Magic Tree House® Merlin Missions and other Magic Tree House® titles, visit MagicTreeHouse.com.

MAGIC
TREE HOUSE®

#7 SUNSET OF THE SABERTOOTH

BY MARY POPE OSBORNE
ILLUSTRATED BY SAL MURDOCCA

A STEPPING STONE BOOK™

Random House 🏠 New York

To all the kids who've helped me

Text copyright © 1996 by Mary Pope Osborne
Cover art and interior illustrations copyright © 1996 by Sal Murdocca
All rights reserved. Published in the United States by Random House Children's Books, a division of Penguin Random House LLC, New York. Originally published in paperback in the United States by Random House Children's Books, New York, in 1996.

Random House and the colophon are registered trademarks and A Stepping Stone Book and the colophon are trademarks of Penguin Random House LLC. Magic Tree House is a registered trademark of Mary Pope Osborne; used under license.

Visit us on the Web!
SteppingStonesBooks.com
randomhousekids.com
MagicTreeHouse.com

Educators and librarians, for a variety of teaching tools, visit us at
RHTeachersLibrarians.com

Library of Congress Cataloging-in-Publication Data
Osborne, Mary Pope. Sunset of the sabertooth / by Mary Pope Osborne ; illustrated by Sal Murdocca.
    p. cm. — (The Magic tree house series ; # 7) "A first stepping stone book."
Summary: The magic tree house transports Jack and Annie on a mission to the Ice Age where they encounter Cro-Magnons, cave bears, sabertooth tigers, and woolly mammoths.
ISBN 978-0-679-86373-1 (trade) — ISBN 978-0-679-96373-8 (lib. bdg.) —
ISBN 978-0-375-89424-4 (ebook)
[1. Prehistoric peoples—Fiction. 2. Prehistoric animals—Fiction. 3. Time travel—Fiction. 4. Magic—Fiction.]
I. Murdocca, Sal, ill. II. Title. III. Series. Osborne, Mary Pope. Magic tree house series ; #7.
PZ7.O81167Su 1996 [Fic]—dc20 95-34697

Printed in the United States of America   61 60 59 58 57

This book has been officially leveled by using the F&P Text Level Gradient™ Leveling System.

Contents

Prologue

One summer day in Frog Creek, Pennsylvania, a mysterious tree house appeared in the woods.

Eight-year-old Jack and his seven-year-old sister, Annie, climbed into the tree house. They found it was filled with books.

Jack and Annie soon discovered that the tree house was magic. It could take them to the places in the books. All they had to do was to point to a picture and wish to go there.

Jack and Annie visited dinosaurs, knights, an Egyptian queen, pirates, ninjas, and the Amazon rain forest.

Along the way, they discovered that the tree house belonged to Morgan le Fay. Morgan was a magical librarian. She traveled through time and space, gathering books for King Arthur's library.

On their fifth adventure, in *Night of the Ninjas*, Jack and Annie found a little mouse in the tree house. Annie named their new friend "Peanut."

Jack and Annie also found a note from Morgan. The note told them that she was under a spell. To free her, Jack and Annie must find four special things.

They found the first thing in old Japan, and the second in the Amazon rain forest.

Now Jack and Annie and Peanut are about to set out in search of the third thing . . . in *Sunset of the Sabertooth*.

1

The "M" Things

"Let's go to the tree house," said Annie.

She and Jack were passing the Frog Creek woods on their way home from their swimming class at the Y.

"No. I want to go home and change out of my bathing suit," said Jack.

"Oh, that'll take too long," said Annie. "Don't you want to save Morgan as soon as possible?"

"Of course," said Jack.

"Then come on! Before the sun sets!" said Annie.

She darted into the woods.

Jack sighed. He gave up on the idea of changing out of his bathing suit.

He pushed his glasses into place. He followed Annie into the Frog Creek woods.

The warm air smelled fresh and green.

He moved through patches of sunlight and shadow. Soon he came to a small clearing.

He looked up. There it was. The magic tree house in the tallest tree in the woods.

"Hurry!" called Annie. She was climbing the rope ladder up to the tree house.

Jack grabbed the ladder. He started up after her.

Finally they reached the tree house.

Squeak. A mouse sat on the window sill.

"Hi, Peanut!" cried Annie.

Jack patted the tiny head.

"Sorry we didn't come sooner," Annie said. "But we had to go to our swimming lesson."

Squeak.

"What happened while we were gone?" asked Annie, looking around the tree house.

Jack stared at the large M carved into the wooden floor.

On the M were a moonstone and a mango, the special things they'd found on their last two journeys.

"Hey, guess what?" said Jack. "*Moonstone* and *mango* start with the letter M. Just like *Morgan*."

"You're right," said Annie.

"I bet all four things start with an M," said Jack.

"Right," said Annie. "I wonder where we'll find the next one."

She and Jack stared at the stacks of books in the tree house. Books on the Amazon rain forest, ninjas, pirates, mummies, knights, and dinosaurs.

All of them were closed. Only one book lay open in the corner.

"We're just about to find out," said Jack.

They walked over to the open book.

They looked at the page the book was opened to. It showed a picture of rocks and snow.

"Wow," said Annie, running her finger over the picture. "I love snow. I wish we could go there right now."

"Wait," said Jack. "We're not prepared." Then he had another thought. "And we're wearing our bathing suits! Stop!"

"Oops," said Annie.

Too late. The wind started to blow.

The leaves started to shake.

The tree house started to spin.

It spun faster and faster!

Then everything was silent.

It was as silent as the falling snow.

2
Bones

Jack, Annie, and Peanut looked outside.

Snow was falling from a gray sky.

The tree house was in the tallest tree in a grove of tall, bare trees.

The grove was on a wide, white plain. Beyond the plain were high, rocky cliffs.

"I'm c-cold," said Annie. Her teeth chattered. She wrapped her towel tightly around her.

Sq-squeak. Peanut sounded cold, too.

"Poor mouse," said Annie. "I'll put you into Jack's pack. You'll be warmer there."

Annie slipped Peanut into the pocket of the backpack.

"We have to go home," said Jack. "We need warmer clothes."

"We can't go home," said Annie. "We can't find the Pennsylvania book. Not until our mission is complete. Remember? That's the way the magic works."

"Oh . . . right," said Jack. He looked around. There was no sign of the Pennsylvania book that always took them home.

Annie peered out the window again. "Where are we, anyway?" she asked.

"I'll find out," said Jack. He picked up the open book and read the title on the cover. "*Life in the Ice Age.*"

"*Ice Age?*" said Annie. "No wonder we're cold."

"We better find the third M thing soon," said Jack. "Before we freeze to death."

"Look," whispered Annie, "people." She pointed out the window.

Jack saw them, too: four figures on a cliff. Two big figures and two little ones—all holding long spears.

"Who are they?" said Annie.

"I'll look in the book," said Jack.

He found a picture of some people. He read the caption to Annie:

> Early modern humans were called Cro-Magnons. During the late Ice Age in Europe, they sometimes lived in caves beneath cliffs.

"Why are they carrying spears?" said Annie.

Jack turned the page. He found another picture of the Cro-Magnons. He read aloud:

> The Cro-Magnon family often hunted together. They covered deep pits with branches. Then they drove reindeer and mammoths into the traps.

"Oh, trapping the animals—that's sad," said Annie.

"No, it's not," said Jack. "They couldn't live without hunting. They didn't have supermarkets, you know."

They watched the family disappear over the other side of the cliff.

"Come on, I'm freezing," said Jack. "Let's hurry and find the M thing while the Cro-Magnons are hunting."

"But I want to meet them," said Annie.

"Forget it," said Jack. "They don't have books that tell them about *us*. They'll think we're some enemy and hurl their spears."

"Yikes," said Annie.

Jack put his book away.

Squeak. Peanut peeked out of the backpack.

"Stay in there," said Annie.

Jack pulled on his pack and started down the rope ladder.

Annie followed.

On the icy ground, they huddled together.

The wind was biting. Jack put his towel over his head. Snow blew against his glasses.

"Hey, Jack," said Annie. "Look at me."

Annie had put on her swimming goggles. "Now I can see," she said.

"Good thinking," said Jack. "Now cover your head with your towel. Most of your body heat is lost through your head."

Annie wrapped her towel around her head.

"We should find a cave or someplace warmer," said Jack.

"I bet there are caves in those cliffs," said Annie.

She and Jack started across the white

16

plain. The snow wasn't deep yet. But the wind was blowing hard.

"I told you!" Annie pointed to an opening in the rocks—a *cave*.

They ran to it.

"Careful," said Jack. They stepped carefully into the shadowy cave.

It was only slightly warmer inside. But at least the wind wasn't blowing.

In the gray light, they stamped the snow off their sneakers.

Annie took off her goggles.

"It smells in here," said Jack.

"Yeah, like a wet dog," said Annie.

"Let me see what I can find out," said Jack.

He pulled out the Ice Age book.

"I'll look around," said Annie. "Maybe the M thing is here. Then we can go home and get warm."

Jack stood by the entrance so he could read the book.

"This cave is filled with sticks," Annie said.

"What?" said Jack. He didn't look up from the book.

"No, wait. I think they're *bones*," said Annie.

"Bones?" echoed Jack.

"Yeah. Lots of them back here. All over the floor."

Jack turned the pages of his book. He found a picture of a cave filled with bones.

"I hear something," said Annie.

Jack read the writing below the picture of the cave. It said:

The great cave bears of the Ice Age
were over eight feet tall. These bears
were larger and fiercer than today's
grizzlies. Their caves were filled with
the bones of their ancestors.

"Annie!" whispered Jack. "Get back here
now!"

They were in the cave of a great cave bear!

3

Brrr!

"Annie!" whispered Jack again.

No answer.

He put his book quietly into his pack. He stepped deeper into the cave.

"Annie!" he said a little louder.

Jack stepped on the bones.

The wet dog smell grew stronger.

He kept going, deeper into the smelly blackness.

He ran into something. He gasped.

"Jack?" said Annie. "Is that you?"

"Didn't you hear me calling?" Jack whispered. "We have to get out of here!"

"Wait," she said. "Someone's sleeping back there. Hear him snoring?"

Jack heard a low, deep moaning. It was loud, then soft. Loud, then soft.

"That's not a person," he said. "It's a great cave bear!"

A booming snore shattered the air.

"Yikes!" said Annie.

"Go! Go!" said Jack.

He and Annie ran through the cave, over the bones, and out into the falling snow.

They kept on going. They ran between fallen rocks and under jagged cliffs.

Finally they stopped and turned around.

All they could see was snow and rocks and their own footprints.

No bear.

"Whew," said Annie. "That was lucky."

"Yeah," said Jack. "He probably never even woke up. We just got in a panic."

Annie huddled close to Jack. "Brrr! I'm f-freezing," she said.

"Me too," he said.

He took off his glasses to wipe off the snow. The cold wind blew against his bare legs.

"Wow," Annie said. "Look." She pointed to something behind Jack.

"What?" Jack put his glasses back on and turned around.

Under a cliff was a wide ledge. Under the ledge was another cave.

Only *this* cave seemed to have a golden glow.

This one looked cozy and safe and warm.

4

Cave Kids

Jack and Annie crept to the cave and peeked inside.

A small flame danced from a bed of glowing coals.

Near the fire were knives, axes, and hollowed-out stones.

Animal skins were neatly stacked against the wall.

"People must live here," said Annie.

"Maybe it's the home of the Cro-Magnons

we saw," said Jack, looking around.

"Let's go inside and get warm," said Annie.

Jack and Annie moved quickly to the fire and warmed their hands.

Their shadows danced on the stone walls.

Jack pulled out his Ice Age book. He found a picture of a cave. He read:

> Cro-Magnons made many things from animals, plants, and stone. They made flute-like musical instruments from mammoth bones. They made ropes by braiding plant fibers. They made axes and knives from stone.

Jack pulled out his notebook and pencil. He started a list:

Cro-Magnons made:
bone flutes
plant ropes
stone axes and knives

"Ta-da!" said Annie.

Jack looked up. Annie was wearing a coat.

It had a hood and long sleeves. It went all the way down to her sneakers.

"Where did you get that?" said Jack.

"From that pile of furry skins," said Annie, pointing. "These must be their clothes. Maybe they're being mended."

She picked up another coat and handed it to Jack.

"Try one. It's really warm," she said.

Jack put his backpack and towel down on the hard dirt floor. He slipped on the coat.

It did feel very warm—and soft.

"We look like cave kids," said Annie.

Squeak. Peanut peeked out of Jack's pack lying on the floor.

"You stay in there," said Annie. "There's no teeny coat for you."

Peanut vanished back into the pack.

"I wonder how they made these coats," said Jack.

He turned the pages in the book until he found a picture of Cro-Magnon women sewing. He read:

> Cro-Magnons scraped reindeer skins
> with flint rocks to make them soft.
> They used bone needles to sew the
> skins together for clothing.

Jack added to his list:

reindeer-skin clothes

"I hope the cave people won't mind if we borrow their coats," said Jack.

"Maybe we should give them our towels," said Annie. "To thank them."

"Good idea."

"And my goggles, too," said Annie.

They left their gifts on top of the rest of the animal skins.

"Let's explore the cave before they come home," said Jack.

"It's too dark in the back," said Annie. "We won't be able to see anything."

"I'll find out how Cro-Magnons saw in the dark," said Jack.

He opened the Ice Age book. He found a picture of cave people holding odd-looking lamps. He read aloud to Annie:

> Cro-Magnons made stone lamps. They
> hollowed out a rock, filled it with
> animal fat, then burned a wick made
> from moss.

"There!" said Annie. She pointed to two stones near the fire. In the hollow of each was gooey white stuff and a pile of moss.

"We have to be careful," said Jack.

He picked up one stone. It was smaller than a soup bowl, but much heavier.

Jack held the stone close to the fire and lit the piece of moss.

He lit another lamp and gave it to Annie.

"Carry it with two hands," he said.

"I know," she said.

Jack tucked the book under his arm. He

and Annie carried their stone lamps to the back of the cave.

"Hey, I wonder where this goes," said Annie. She held her lamp up to an opening in the wall.

"I'll check in the book," said Jack.

He put down his lamp and flipped through the Ice Age book.

"I think it's a tunnel," she said. "Be right back."

"Wait a second," said Jack.

Too late—she had squeezed into the opening and was gone.

"Oh brother," said Jack, sighing.

He closed his book and peeked into the opening.

"Come back here!" he said.

"No! You come *here!*" said Annie. Her voice

sounded far away. "You won't believe this!"

Jack picked up his lamp and book. He ducked into a small tunnel.

"Wow!" came Annie's voice.

Jack could see her lamp flickering at the other end.

Crouching clown, he hurried toward her. At the end of the tunnel was a huge cavern with a high ceiling.

Annie held her lamp close to the wall.

"Look," she said. Her voice echoed.

Animals were painted on the wall in strokes of red and black and yellow.

There were cave bears and lions, elk and reindeer, bison and woolly rhinos and mammoths.

In the flickering light, the prehistoric beasts looked alive.

5
Snow Tracks

"Wow, what is this place?" said Jack.

"Maybe it's an art gallery," said Annie.

"I don't think so," said Jack. "It's too hard to get to."

He read about the cave paintings:

> These Ice Age beasts were painted
> 25,000 years ago. Cro-Magnons painted
> pictures of animals they hunted. They
> may have believed the paintings would
> give them power over the animals.

"Wow, look at this," said Annie.

She pointed at a painting farther down the wall.

It showed a figure with human arms and legs, reindeer antlers, and an owl face. It seemed to be holding a flute.

Jack looked at the book again. He found a picture of the figure and read:

> Cave men may have been led by a sorcerer, or "Master of the Animals." He may have worn reindeer antlers so he could run like a reindeer—and an owl mask so he could see like an owl.

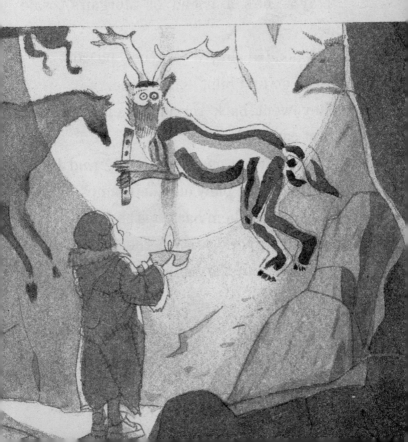

"What is it?" said Annie.

"The Master of the Animals," said Jack. "He's a sorcerer."

"Oh wow," breathed Annie. "That's it."

"That's what?"

"That's who we have to find."

"Why?"

"Maybe he's a friend of Morgan's," said Annie.

Jack nodded slowly. "Maybe," he said.

"Let's go find him," said Annie.

They went back through the tunnel into the first cave.

"We better put our lamps back," said Jack.

He and Annie blew out their lamps.

They placed them back by the fire.

Jack's backpack was on the floor next to the skins. He put the Ice Age book into it.

"How's Peanut?" said Annie.

Jack looked into his pack. "She's not here," he said.

"Oh no!" cried Annie. "She must have crawled out when we were looking at the paintings."

"Peanut!" Jack called.

"Peanut!" called Annie.

Annie walked slowly around the cave, looking into the shadows.

Jack peered around the fire and under each of the furry skins.

"Jack! Come here!" said Annie.

She was standing near the entrance to the cave.

The snow had stopped falling.

In the snow were tiny tracks.

6
Song on the Wind

"Peanut's tracks," said Annie. "We have to find her before she freezes."

She wrapped her reindeer coat around her and headed across the snow.

Jack pulled on his backpack and followed.

The mouse's tracks led them between the fallen rocks and back onto the open plain.

The wind blew harder. Snow swirled over the ground, covering the tiny footprints.

"I can't see them anymore!" wailed Annie.

She and Jack now stood in the middle of the plain. They stared at the windswept snow.

The mouse's tracks had vanished.

"Yikes," whispered Annie, staring up.

Jack followed her gaze. On one of the cliffs was a tiger. A giant tiger with two long, sharp fangs.

"A *sabertooth*," said Jack.

"I hope he doesn't see us," whispered Annie.

"Me too," Jack whispered back. "We'd better head back to the tree house."

Jack and Annie stepped very softly across the snow. Then Jack glanced back at the cliff.

The sabertooth was gone.

"Oh man," he said. "Where is he?"

"Run to the trees!" said Annie.

He and Annie started running. They ran over the snowy plain, heading toward the tall, bare trees in the distance.

Suddenly Jack heard a *crack*.

The ground caved in, and Jack went with it.

Annie fell beside him.

They crashed down onto a heap of branches, snow, and earth.

They struggled to stand. Jack pushed his glasses into place.

"You all right?" he asked Annie.

"Yes," she said.

They both looked up. They were in a deep hole. All Jack could see were gray clouds moving overhead.

"This is a trap," Jack said. "The Cro-

Magnons must have put branches over this hole. Then the snow hid the branches. So we didn't see them."

"There's no way out," said Annie.

She was right. They were helpless. The pit was too deep to climb out of.

"I feel like a trapped animal," Annie said.

"Me too," said Jack.

He heard a yowl in the distance.

"The sabertooth!" whispered Annie.

Jack pulled out the Ice Age book. He found a picture of the sabertooth. He read:

> The sabertooth was the fiercest beast of the Ice Age. It attacked humans as well as woolly mammoths and other large animals.

"Oh brother," said Jack.

"Listen!" Annie grabbed him.

"What?" Jack jumped.

"I hear music."

Jack listened. But all he heard was the wind.

"You hear it?" said Annie.

"No," said Jack.

"Listen carefully."

He closed his eyes. He listened very carefully.

He heard the wind. But this time he heard another sound, too.

Strange, haunting music.

"Ahhh!" cried Annie.

Jack opened his eyes.

Staring down at them was a figure wearing reindeer antlers and an owl mask.

"The sorcerer," whispered Jack.

Squeak.

Peanut peered down at them, too!

7

The Sorcerer's Gift

The sorcerer didn't speak. He stared through the eyeholes of the owl mask.

"Help us, please," said Annie.

The sorcerer threw a rope into the pit. Jack grabbed it.

"He wants to pull us up," said Annie.

Jack looked up. The sorcerer was gone.

"Where did he go?" Jack said.

"Tug on the rope," said Annie.

Jack tugged. The rope tightened. It began rising.

"I'll go first!" said Annie cheerfully.

"Annie, this isn't a game," warned Jack.

"Don't worry, I'll be careful."

Jack gave her the rope. "Okay. But hold on tight," he said.

Annie held the rope with both hands. She pushed her feet against the side of the pit. She rose into the air with the rope.

She kept pressing against the side of the pit—until she reached the top.

Jack saw the sorcerer reappear and help Annie up. Then they moved out of sight.

Jack was puzzled. The sorcerer had used both hands to help Annie. So who held the other end of the rope?

"Wow!" came Annie's voice.

What's going on? Jack wondered.

The sorcerer came back and threw the rope down again.

Jack grabbed it. And the rope started to rise.

Jack held on tight. He started up. His hands burned. His arms felt as if they were being pulled out of their sockets.

But he kept his hold on the rope and his feet against the side of the pit.

At the top the sorcerer pulled Jack onto the snowy ground.

"Thanks," said Jack, standing.

The sorcerer was tall. He wore a long fur robe. Jack could see only his eyes through the owl mask.

"Hey!" Annie called.

Jack turned.

Annie was sitting on a woolly mammoth.

Squeak. Peanut was sitting on the mammoth's head.

The mammoth looked like a giant elephant with shaggy reddish hair and long, curved tusks.

The other end of the rope was around the mammoth's huge neck.

"Lulu pulled us up," said Annie.

"Lulu?" said Jack.

"Don't you think she looks like a Lulu?" said Annie.

"Oh brother," said Jack. He walked up to the mammoth.

"Hey, mammoth starts with M," said Annie. "Maybe Lulu's the special thing!"

"I don't think so," said Jack.

The great creature knelt down, just like a circus elephant.

"Whoa!" said Annie. She clutched the mammoth's ears to keep from falling off.

The sorcerer helped Jack climb onto the mammoth.

"Thanks," said Jack.

Then the sorcerer reached into a pouch. He pulled out a smooth white bone and handed it to Jack.

The bone was hollow. It had four holes along one side. And two on the other.

"Oh man, I think it's his flute," said Jack. "The book said they make flutes from mammoth bones."

Jack tried to give the flute back to the sorcerer.

"Nice," he said politely.

But the sorcerer held up his hand.

"He wants you to keep the mammoth bone," said Annie.

"*Mammoth bone*," whispered Jack. "Hey, maybe this is the third thing."

Jack looked at the sorcerer. "Do you know Morgan?" he asked.

The sorcerer did not answer. But his eyes sparkled with kindness.

He turned away from Jack and untied the mammoth's rope. Then he whispered in the ear of the giant woolly creature.

When the mammoth stood up, Jack gripped Annie's coat to keep from falling off. He felt miles above the ground.

He nestled behind Annie, in the dip between the mammoth's head and huge curved back.

The mammoth took slow, plodding steps across the snow, then picked up speed.

"Where are we going?" said Jack as they bumped up and down.

"To the tree house!" said Annie.

"How does he know where it is?" said Jack.

"*She* just knows," said Annie.

Jack looked back.

The sorcerer was standing in the snow, watching them.

But at that moment the clouds parted, and the sun came out.

Jack was blinded by sunlight on the snow.

He squinted to see—but the sorcerer had vanished.

8

The Great Parade

The huge mammoth walked across the open plain.

"Look!" said Annie. She pointed to a herd of elk in the distance. They had great, wide antlers.

"There!" said Jack as a herd of reindeer came into view. They pranced gracefully across the snow.

Then a woolly rhino joined them on the open plain. Then a bison!

The elk, reindeer, rhino, and bison moved along with them, at a distance.

They seemed to be escorting Jack and Annie back to the tree house.

The snow sparkled with sunlight.

This is a great parade, Jack thought. *Fantastic.*

They were getting closer and closer to the grove of tall trees.

"I told you," said Annie. "Lulu's taking us home."

But just then the mammoth let out a cry. All the other animals bounded off.

Peanut started to squeak.

Jack looked around.

Behind them the sabertooth was slinking across the sunlit snow!

The woolly mammoth roared and plunged forward.

Jack and Annie nearly fell off.

Jack clutched Annie. She and Peanut clutched the mammoth's shaggy hair.

The mammoth thundered wildly over the ground.

"Ahhh!" Jack and Annie yelled.

The mammoth charged to the grove of trees.

But the tiger had circled around the trees. He stood between the tallest tree and the mammoth.

They were trapped.

The sabertooth began moving slowly toward the mammoth.

The woolly mammoth roared fiercely.

But Jack knew a sabertooth could kill any creature, including a mammoth.

The huge tiger's head was down. His burning eyes were fixed on the mammoth. His long white fangs glinted in the sunlight.

9
Master of the Animals

The sabertooth crept forward.

Jack stared in horror.

"Play the flute," whispered Annie.

Is she nuts? Jack thought.

"Try!" said Annie.

Jack held the mammoth-bone flute to his lips. He blew.

The flute made a strange sound.

The tiger froze. He glared at Jack.

Jack's hands shook.

The tiger growled. He took another step.

The mammoth roared and stomped the ground.

"Play it!" said Annie. "Keep playing!"

Jack blew again.

The sabertooth froze again.

Jack kept blowing until he ran out of breath.

The tiger snarled.

"He's still here," whispered Annie. "Keep it up."

Jack closed his eyes. He took a deep breath. Then he blew as hard and as long as he could. He covered and uncovered the holes on the bone.

The music sounded strange—as if it were coming from another world.

"He's leaving!" Annie whispered.

Jack raised his eyes. The sabertooth was slinking off toward the cliffs.

"We did it!" said Annie.

Jack lowered the flute. He felt very tired.

The mammoth waved her trunk happily.

"To the tree house, Lulu," said Annie.

The woolly mammoth snorted. Then she lumbered over to the tallest tree.

From the back of the mammoth, Jack grabbed the rope ladder. He held it for Annie.

She stroked the mammoth's giant ear. "Bye, Lulu. Thank you," she said.

Annie grabbed the rope ladder. Then she started up. Peanut climbed up, too.

After they disappeared into the tree house, Jack climbed onto the ladder.

He looked back at the woolly mammoth.

"Bye, girl," he said. "Go home now. And watch out for the sabertooth."

The mammoth walked away into the sunset.

When Jack couldn't see her anymore, he started up the lope ladder. He pulled himself into the tree house.

"Ta-da!" said Annie. She handed the Pennsylvania book to Jack.

Jack smiled. Now he was positive they had found the third M thing. Their mission was complete.

"Before we leave, we have to give our coats back," said Annie.

"Oh right," said Jack.

They took off their reindeer-skin coats and dropped them to the ground.

"Brrr!" said Annie. "I hope the Cro-Magnon people find them."

Jack stared out the window. He wanted to take one last look at the prehistoric world.

The sun was setting behind the hills. Four people were crossing the snowy plain. It was the Cro-Magnon family.

"Hey!" shouted Annie.

"Shhh!" said Jack.

The Cro-Magnons stopped and peered in Annie and Jack's direction.

"We left your reindeer skins! Down there!" Annie pointed to the ground.

The tallest person stepped forward and raised a spear.

"Time to go," said Jack.

He grabbed the Pennsylvania book. He

found the picture of Frog Creek and pointed at it. "I wish we could go home," he said.

"Good-bye! Good luck!" Annie called, waving out the window.

The wind started to blow. And the tree house started to spin.

It spun faster and faster.

Then everything was still.

Absolutely still.

10
This Age

Birds sang. The air was soft and warm.

"I hope they find their coats," said Annie.

"Me too," said Jack. He pushed his glasses into place.

Squeak.

"Hey, you—how did you find the sorcerer?" Annie asked Peanut.

Squeak.

"It's a secret, huh?" said Annie. She turned to Jack. "Where's the flute?"

He held up the mammoth bone. Then he placed it on the M carved into the floor. Next to the mango from the rain forest. Next to the moonstone from the time of ninjas.

"Moonstone, mango, mammoth bone . . ."
Annie said. "We need just one more M thing.
Then Morgan will be free from her spell."

"Tomorrow," said Jack.

Annie patted Peanut on the head. "Bye,
you," she said.

She started down the rope ladder.

Jack gathered his things.

He paused and glanced at the mouse. She
stared at him with big brown eyes.

"Thanks again for helping us," he said.

Then he climbed down the rope ladder and
jumped onto the ground.

Jack and Annie ran through the Frog
Creek woods onto their street.

Their neighborhood looked rosy in the
sunset.

It's great to be back in this age, Jack

thought. *Warm and safe and almost home.*

"I'm glad we don't have to go hunting for dinner," he said.

"Yeah, Mom and Dad already did that," said Annie, "at the supermarket."

"I hope they trapped some spaghetti and meatballs," said Jack.

"I hope they trapped a pizza," said Annie.

"Hurry, I'm starving," said Jack.

They ran up their sidewalk and through their front door.

"We're home!" shouted Annie.

"What's for dinner?" shouted Jack.

Here's a special preview of
Magic Tree House® Fact Tracker

Sabertooths
and the Ice Age

After their adventure with Lulu the woolly
mammoth, Jack and Annie wanted to know more
about the Ice Age. Track the facts with them!

Available now!

Excerpt copyright © 2005 by Mary Pope Osborne and Natalie Pope Boyce.
Illustrations copyright © 2005 by Sal Murdocca. Published by Random House
Children's Books, a division of Penguin Random House LLC, New York.

Ice Age Campsite

Hides were stretched on a frame.

Researchers have found piles of flint chips from making tools.

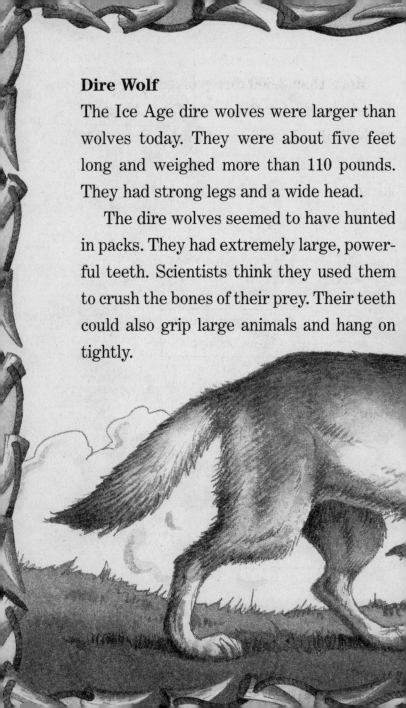

Dire Wolf

The Ice Age dire wolves were larger than wolves today. They were about five feet long and weighed more than 110 pounds. They had strong legs and a wide head.

The dire wolves seemed to have hunted in packs. They had extremely large, powerful teeth. Scientists think they used them to crush the bones of their prey. Their teeth could also grip large animals and hang on tightly.

More than 3,600 dire wolves have been found in the La Brea Tar Pits. Many of their skulls show signs of injury. Scientists think they got these wounds from being kicked in the head by animals they were attacking.